THE LANDSCAPES OF SOUTHERN ALBERTA

A Regional Geomorphology

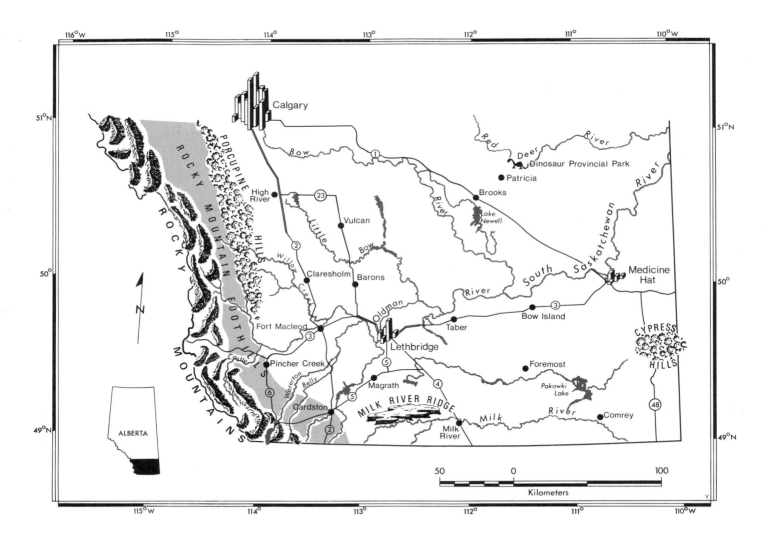

THE LANDSCAPES OF SOUTHERN ALBERTA

A Regional Geomorphology

Chester B. Beaty
Department of Geography
University of Lethbridge

Photographs by the author

Maps and diagrams by G. Stanley Young
Department of Geography
University of Lethbridge

Dedicated to the taxpayers of Alberta, particularly those of the south, who have provided a comfortable salary and excellent working conditions for six years and deserve something tangible for their money.

Second Printing, 1976
Third Printing, 1979
Fourth Printing, 1984
Fifth Printing, 1989

The University of Lethbridge
Printing Services

ISBN #0-919555-61-6

CONTENTS

INTRODUCTION

The science of landscape study is known as *geomorphology*. The geomorphologist, accordingly, is simply one who devotes all or most of his professional time to an attempt at reaching an understanding of how parts of the earth's surface have acquired the landscape characteristics we observe today. Geomorphologists come in assorted sizes and shapes and from a variety of academic backgrounds. Most have received formal instruction and training in the traditional disciplines of geography and geology, but some of the more imaginative students of landscape have wandered into the field by way of seemingly unrelated professional interests. Whatever the formal or informal background, however, all share a common concern about the details of the solid surface of the earth — its shape, the materials of which it is made, the processes operating through time responsible for its contemporary condition, and, on occasion, the possible future changes that may occur. Geomorphology is thus an integral part of the group of studies known collectively as the *earth sciences*.

The present volume represents a relatively modest attempt to describe and explain the landscapes, or geomorphology, of southern Alberta. "Southern Alberta", as defined for our purposes, includes all of the province south of an east-west line running approximately through High River and Brooks. The northern boundary is arbitrary, of course, and is based primarily upon the author's knowledge (or ignorance) of the area in question. The other boundaries are political lines, in no case coinciding with an easily recognizable change in scenery. Southern Alberta, thus delimited, is obviously a classic example of a non-region, lacking overall internal homogeneity and not separated from adjacent parts of North America by conspicuous variations in the major physical features, including land forms. So it is readily conceded that the "region" implied by the title lacks any sort of rigorous, clear-cut definition.

And yet there *are* differences as one moves away from the heart of southern Alberta, some merely of degree, some of considerably more substantial import. Changes in climate, changes in basic geologic structure and rock type, changes in land use — all contribute ultimately to changes in total landscape. Especially as climate and geology change, so do surface processes and forms. Thus, although the "pure" regional geographer may object strenuously to the concept of a southern Alberta region, the area does have distinctive characteristics, both natural and man-made, that justify its treatment as a discrete and identifiable geographic and geomorphologic entity.

This book, then, will be dealing with the variegated landscapes of a relatively small but fascinating part of the North American continent. Plains, foothills, and mountains constitute the basic elements of southern Alberta, and each unit, or geomorphologic region, differs from its neighbors by virtue of variations in topography, fundamental geologic structure and history, and operation and intensity of present-day processes of change. An east-west transect through southern Alberta clearly reveals that the differences in landscape are real and often dramatic, and these differences, and the reasons therefore, are a major theme in this volume.

A few words are in order about the "why?" of a book of this sort. In recent years an incredible amount of unadulterated nonsense has been cranked out concerning man-land relationships and the dire future awaiting foolish, wasteful, polluting humankind on this planet. There seems to be an unwritten belief that somehow, although exactly *how* is never very clearly spelled out, if only enough people read enough books about matters environmental and/or ecological, it may be possible to avoid global catastrophe. If salvation depends primarily on the number of "disaster" books that have already been thrust upon the public, then our future seems assured.

Well, this book is not of that particular persuasion. There is no poignant environmental message herein, nor do I have a universal panacea to offer for the woes of 20th century civilization. The emphasis is on landscapes — what they look like, how they got that way, and (in a very few instances) what might happen to them in the geologically foreseeable future. Although the point can be and undoubtedly has been overworked, it is my firm conviction that some knowledge of the physical world in which we live is a useful acquisition for anyone, leading to a richer and much more interesting life. It so happens that southern Alberta has experienced a remarkably diverse geologic and geomorphologic history, the results of which are visible and recognizable in the landscapes of the present. A general understanding of these landscapes is the goal — they are worth study and attention simply because they are there.

A Note about the Photographs:

Most of the pictures in this volume were made from locations on or near major highways or secondary roads, the idea being to illustrate various aspects of southern Alberta geomorphology as viewed by most residents in their day-to-day working or vacationing lives. A few photographs required a certain amount of walking or climbing, and several were taken from the air, but the vast majority portray elements of the landscapes in which we spend much of our time, seeing or not seeing as the case may be.

CHAPTER 1
SURFACE PROCESS AND FORM

The landscapes of any part of the earth's surface consist of *forms* made by *processes* acting on *materials* through *time*. Form, process, materials, and time thus constitute the geomorphologic Big Four. Of these, probably time, for the average person, is initially the most difficult concept to come to grips with, since earth scientists tend to use a time scale that seems enormously long by human standards. For example, in an article in a recent issue of the journal *Science* the term "the present" was used to refer to the last 10 million years of earth history. Accordingly, what is "young" to a geologist may well be an event or particular rock formation several tens of millions of years old, and when a geomorphologist speaks or writes of "rapid change", he often will be describing a sequence of related landscape alterations encompassing hundreds of thousands of years.

On the other hand, it is perfectly obvious to layman and scientist alike that the occasional event will be rapid and catastrophic, although the geologic record strongly suggests that such sudden, dramatic episodes have been relatively rare in the long history of the earth. So far as southern Alberta is concerned, evidence of violent, cataclysmic change is virtually non-existent. Implicit in a majority of studies of the earth's landscapes is a basic geologic tenet: The present is the key to the past. Simply put, this suggests that the origin of most contemporary land forms can satisfactorily be explained in terms of the operation of processes we can see in action today, although in the past not necessarily all with the same intensity as now. Serious students of landscape evolution have concluded that explanations based on geologic catastrophes in some near or distant time are usually not required.

Earth scientists customarily think of the surface forms of this planet as being the result of a never-ending contest between two opposing sets of processes of change. These are: (1) the *internal* or *tectonic processes,* powered primarily by energy generated and released within the solid body of the earth; and (2) the *external* or *gradational processes,* controlled, in the main, by two factors, *gravity* and *climate.* The internal processes operate basically to create *relief* (which is the vertical distance from the lowest to the highest elevation in a given area), to elevate parts of the crust, either by the addition of new rock material at the surface (a process known as vulcanism) or by contortion or uplift of parts of the crust without conspicuous volcanic activity (a process labeled *diastrophism*). Of the two, diastrophism appears to have been by far the more important over the long course of earth history, although from time to time and place to place, vulcanism has produced spectacular results in a period amounting to little more than a geologic snap of the fingers. Types of tectonic activity and their effects will be discussed in the next chapter.

In marked contrast to relief-building tectonism, the external processes lead to a wearing down or lowering of high-standing parts of the crust. Functioning to counteract the results of internal activity, they operate to smooth out the surface, to bring it to grade, generally sea level. Most of us are more familiar with the gradational forces and processes because these are what we see in action, in one way or another, almost every day of our lives. In southern Alberta, for example, the larger and smaller rivers and streams are readily visible *(Figure 1),* and the geomorphologic work they accomplish is relatively easily observed and understood.

Geomorphologists are particularly interested in the gradational (or external) forces and processes, since most land forms are the product of active gradation working on comparatively passive tectonic structures. In any given part of the earth's crust, most internal forces tend to operate intermittently, at least over short to intermediate spans of geologic time, whereas the external processes, powered by and related to gravity and climate, are free to function more or less continuously. The condition and shape of most landscapes usually reflect the type and intensity of operation of the most recently effective gradational processes, including those that are active today.

What are the gradational forces and processes? The rivers and streams of southern Alberta have been mentioned, and certainly *running water,* in all of its manifestations, is believed by many students of landscape to be the most important agent of gradation in large segments of the earth's surface. Other agents are the *wind, glacial ice, waves and currents,* and, acting to create a very special set of land forms, *gravity* itself. The landscapes of southern Alberta have been shaped, in one way or another, by the activities of all of these forces of change.

Figure 1. Valley of the St. Mary River south of Lethbridge.

Running Water

The streams of the earth, whether large or small, are capable of performing three essential geomorphologic chores: They *erode* materials from their beds and banks, they *transport* rock and mineral debris toward and ultimately into bodies of standing water, and they *deposit* boulders, gravel, sand, silt, and clay along their courses and at the end of flow. Stream behavior is complex and has been studied intensively for both theoretical and practical purposes. A number of aspects of stream activity are incompletely understood, but basically the amount of geomorphologic work a stream can do is most directly related to its *discharge,* the volume of water per unit of time flowing through the channel at a given place.

The single most important characteristic of stream flow is *velocity,* since this conditions how much and what kind of geologic work a stream is capable of accomplishing. Whatever the size of a stream, as its velocity increases so does its ability to pick up and keep moving rock material of increasing size. Rock and mineral debris in transit in a stream is referred to as its *load,* which consists of three components: the *dissolved* or *chemical load,* the *suspended load* (material held up in the body of the stream that accounts for the roily or muddy appearance of many rivers), and the *bed load,* made of debris moving on or close to the floor of the channel. Dissolved and suspended loads are relatively easily measured by systematic sampling at selected depths within a stream, but accurate determination of the bed load is much more difficult.

Based on measurements of total load carried by many different rivers, estimates have been made of the average rate of lowering of land surfaces in various parts of the earth; these give values ranging from less than an inch per thousand years in relatively flat terrain to more than a foot per millenium on steep mountain slopes. Whatever the precise figures may be, it seems apparent that the Rockies and foothills of southern Alberta are being worn down much more rapidly than the gently rolling plains.

How effectively a stream may be eroding its bed and banks and thus deepening and perhaps widening its channel depends upon a number of factors, including its velocity, how much load it is already carrying, and the nature of the material into which the channel is being cut. Velocity is especially important since it determines the intensity of *turbulence,* the tendency of fluids to move in a highly irregular, swirling, eddying fashion. It is primarily pressures exerted by turbulently flowing water against the sides and floor of a channel that enable a stream to erode by dislodging material and incorporating it into its load. As velocity increases, turbulence becomes more intense, so most streams are capable of increasingly effective erosion when their discharge rises. At the same time, their ability to transport debris increases proportionately, so it is not surprising that the typical river does by far the greater part of its geomorphologic work when in flood.

The material transported by a stream will sooner or later be deposited, in most cases because of a decrease in velocity and an associated decrease in its ability to move all or part of its load. Streams may thus deposit rock and mineral fragments anywhere along their courses in stretches with reduced velocity; deposition is not limited only to a zone at the end of flow. Stream-deposited materials reflect the relationship between velocity and ability to transport rock debris — as velocity falls, for whatever reason, the largest particles in the load are deposited first, followed by increasingly smaller sizes. Stream-deposited sediments tend to be layered (or stratified) and are usually sorted or segregated on a size basis into beds of gravel, sand, and silts and clays. In this respect they differ notably from debris deposited directly by glacial ice.

The streams and rivers of the earth, flowing in more or less permanent systems of organized channels, are of major importance in the grand scheme of gradation on our planet. By eroding their courses, transporting the materials thus removed, and ultimately depositing the debris in their loads, they sculpture and transform landscapes, functioning in conjunction with one or more of the other agents of gradation to bring about constant change. Their role in the evolution and alteration of the landscapes of southern Alberta will be more fully explored in succeeding chapters.

Wind

Anyone present in southern Alberta for more than just a quiet day or so is only too aware of the wind. As an agent of gradation, the wind shares with running water a number of common characteristics, all related to the fact that both are moving fluids, the behavior of which is controlled by certain basic physical laws. As is true of the streams of the earth, the ability of wind to do geomorphologic work is directly related to its velocity; the stronger the wind, the greater its potential for effective geomorphologic activity. Similarly, the size of materials at the earth's surface determines what can and will

be moved by the wind; even the most powerful blasts are incapable of shifting larger gravel and boulders. Accordingly, most of the surficial debris susceptible to wind action is sand size or smaller.

The geologic work of the wind is twofold: (1) *Deflation* is the removal and transportation of loose surficial materials by the wind, in the course of which a number of interesting landscape features may be made; and (2) *deposition* of debris transported by the wind (in response to a decrease in velocity) produces an equally interesting set of land forms, most of which can be categorized as *dunes* of one sort or another.

It seems highly probable that the geomorphologic effectiveness of the wind has been vastly overrated by many people. The mental image of the typical desert — mostly sand dunes, palm trees, and an occasional heavily robed character on a camel — fostered and conditioned by the Hollywood stereotype, is, in the main, simply wrong. Undeniably there are enormous regions of active sand dunes in some deserts of the Old World. On the other hand, the rather special requirements for effective wind action (including the presence of loose, dry, unprotected surficial materials of the right size in an area of strong, persistent winds) assure that on a world-wide scale only comparatively limited regions are dominated by wind-related landscape features.

Nevertheless, the wind in southern Alberta has been responsible, directly or indirectly, for the development of a number of interesting land forms, and these will be considered in some detail in the discussion of the plains.

Glacial Ice

Most of the southern Alberta landscape has been affected in one way or another by glaciation. Indeed, large portions of this part of the province (and most of the rest) are today much as they were only some 10,000 to 15,000 years ago, when the most recent of the great continental and mountain glaciers disappeared. Glaciation is a dominant theme in coming to an understanding of the what, why, and how of our contemporary scene and will be accorded a prominent place in considerations of landscape origin.

Earth scientists interested in ice as a gradational agent have divided the glaciers of the world (past and present) into two broad categories, *continental* and *valley glaciers* (the latter are also known as *mountain* or *alpine* glaciers). The distinction is not absolute, of course, but the differences between the two major types are real.

Valley glaciers, as the term suggests, are generally confined to canyon-like drainage systems in mountainous regions, and it seems probable that most glaciated valleys existed as stream-cut features before being occupied by ice. Alpine glaciers form at high elevations within the mountains; the movement of the ice is down-valley in a linear fashion, and the pre-existent canyon may be considerably modified by glacial action. If such a glacier extends into a lowland beyond the confines of its valley, its lower end may expand in lobe- or bulb-like fashion to become a *piedmont* glacier. Ice masses originating in the Rockies of southern Alberta are referred to as *Cordilleran* glaciers.

Continental glaciers are, expectably, much larger than individual valley glaciers, spreading over literally hundreds of thousands of square miles, as is the case today with the Greenland and Antarctic ice sheets. Approximately the northern two-thirds of North America was covered by this continent's major ice sheet, the *Laurentide* glacier; the modern Missouri and Ohio rivers roughly define the southern limits of the Laurentide ice. Continental glaciers are thought to evolve initially as relatively small masses of ice in local highlands that subsequently grow and expand into enormous glaciers of great thickness (up to two miles), with radial movement outward in all directions from the center of accumulation. The Laurentide glacier, for example, is believed to have originated mainly in the mountainous terrain of the central Labrador peninsula, with possibly a secondary focus of accumulation west of Hudson Bay. Smaller masses of ice resting on elevated, plateau-like surfaces in mountainous regions are known as *ice caps*; the Columbia Ice Field of Alberta and British Columbia is a nearby example.

A great diversity of land forms is associated with glaciation. A simplified but useful classification scheme includes two general subdivisions, *erosional* and *depositional* forms. The erosional features are perhaps more common in (but by no means restricted to) areas of glacial origin. In these, moving ice was able to strip away pre-glacial soils and, armoured with a load of fragmental debris, abrade the underlying bedrock. Depositional forms are probably best developed at or near the outer limits of glaciation, although a shrinking glacier will often leave behind a contracting zone of depositional features roughly concentric to its place of ultimate extinction.

Debris deposited directly from glacial ice is known as *till*. Till differs markedly from water-deposited sediments in displaying an almost complete lack of stratification and sorting on a particle-size basis. Till consists of a heterogeneous mass of earth materials ranging in size from the finest clays to boulders as large as a house. Glacial meltwater is also capable of constructing a wide variety of depositional features; such *outwash* forms differ from most till in being made predominantly of crudely sorted and stratified debris.

An especially interesting feature of late-glacial and immediate post-glacial time in the southern Alberta plains was the development of a number of extensive but shallow meltwater lakes ponded between the margin of the retreating Laurentide glacier and higher ground to the west and southwest. The lakes were systematically drained as the ice margin receded to the east and northeast. As a result, sizable areas of lake-bed sediments and a remarkable series of drainage channels (Chin and the other large coulees of the prairie) were formed in what was probably a rather short period of time. These land forms constitute some of the most fascinating features of the region; their origin will be described in the chapter on the plains.

The landscapes of southern Alberta have been affected by both alpine and continental glaciation. The Rocky Mountains and parts of the Foothills Belt supported integrated systems of valley glaciers, some of which extended as piedmont glaciers several miles into the plains. Ice of the Laurentide glacier, attaining a thickness of 1,000-2,500 feet, covered all of the plains except for two limited areas, (1) the top of the Cypress Hills upland, and (2) an irregular zone in the southwest extending approximately from Del Bonita to Whiskey Gap and including parts of the west end of Milk River Ridge. It can thus be readily appreciated why evolution of the modern scenery of this part of the province is so intimately related to events of the Ice Age.

Waves and Currents

Land forms of the coasts of the earth reflect the gradational work of waves and currents. Implicit in the idea of a special suite of coastal forms is the existence of a body of standing water (a lake or ocean), the level of which is more or less fixed. Since lakes are inevitably temporary features (in the geologic sense of the word "temporary"), to be destroyed in time by infilling and/or draining, and since general sea level is known to have fluctuated significantly throughout earth history, coastal land forms are far from being permanent features.

Field investigations in all parts of the earth have established beyond doubt that contemporary world-wide sea level was attained only some 4,000-6,000 years ago. At the time of maximum extension of the most recent major continental glaciation, sea level was several hundred feet lower. The reason is simple: So much water was removed from the world ocean and locked up in the form of land ice that the total volume available to fill the ocean basins was significantly reduced. As the great continental glaciers of North America and Eurasia disappeared (for reasons not at all well understood), water was returned to the oceans and sea level rose, stabilizing at approximately its present position a few thousand years ago.

Land forms made by waves and currents are a very minor part of the southern Alberta landscape, primarily because large bodies of standing water have here been short-lived, at best. Mention has been made of shallow lakes present in the plains during late- and post-glacial time. These were evidently of such brief duration that few conspicuous and readily recognizable wave-built or current-related features were formed. Our knowledge of the existence of the lakes is based upon (1) recognition of sediments that accumulated on their beds (largely fine-grained materials such as silts and clays), (2) the very smooth, nearly horizontal surfaces of the upper layers of these deposits, and (3) the interesting series of channels cut in part by the drainage of the lakes. Most of these channels, including Chin, Etzikom, and Verdigris coulees, are dry valleys today. Although there can be no doubt about the reality of the lakes, such typical wave-built forms as beach lines or sand-bar features are generally absent.

There is thus not a great deal to say about the gradational work of waves and currents in our part of the world. On the other hand, formation of the meltwater lakes and their associated channels will constitute an important element in the history of southern Alberta's landscape evolution.

Gravity

The effect of gravity inevitably is present in the operation of all of the agents of gradation previously discussed. But gravity also functions as a propelling force in the downward movement of earth materials in which no conspicuous medium of transporation (water, air, ice) is involved. Downslope movements induced directly by gravity are known as *mass movements* and may be divided into three types or categories: *free fall, landslides,* and *soil creep* (or simply, *creep*). Distinctions among the three are not always clear-cut and absolute, but "textbook" examples of each are easily recognized as being different from the other two.

Free fall is just what the term implies — the free, or essentially free, dropping of a piece of earth material downslope from the position it previously occupied. If a block of rock is detached from a cliff, it obviously falls *down* in response to the pull of gravity. Where many such blocks accumulate near the base of a steep slope, the growing pile of loose, fragmental debris is known as *talus (Figure 2)*; the terms *slide rock* and *scree* are also used. Free fall is thus a comparatively rapid form of mass movement, resulting in the block-by-block building up of what may in time become very impressive bodies of talus. In southern Alberta, recently deglaciated valleys in the Rockies tend to display massive accumulations of talus, especially near their heads where steep bedrock slopes were uncovered as the ice disappeared.

Landslides are a form of mass movement in which sizable volumes of rock or soil move downslope, usually starting as coherent masses but in some cases subsequently breaking into innumerable smaller pieces as a consequence of movement. There is no single landslide classification scheme universally accepted by earth scientists and engineers. The classification

Figure 2. Talus accumulation near the base of Bluff (Goat) Mountain west of Frank. The sloping pile of talus consists of debris that has fallen from the steeper slope above.

system used here is based primarily on (1) the dominant type of material involved, *rock* or *soil* ("soil" in this context referring to all unconsolidated debris on top of hard, unweathered bedrock), and (2) secondarily on the kind of movement sustained, *fall, flow,* or *slump.* This, then, gives rise to the following types of landslides:

Rock fall	Soil flow
Rock flow	Soil slump
Rock slump	

There is no "soil fall" category because unconsolidated earth materials lack the coherence literally to fall in one piece; flowage or slumpage of soil, on the other hand, is relatively common.

In the case of *rock fall, rock flow,* and *soil flow,* the material involved is broken up in the course of downslope movement, even though initially it may have started as an unfragmented block. In *rock slump* and *soil slump,* coherence is generally maintained in the moving block, and backward rotation often accompanies downslope displacement. Quite apparently, movement in some landslides will consist of fall, flowing, and slumping; transitional cases are only to be expected *(Figure 3).*

Soil creep refers to the slowest mass movements of all, those that shift earth materials downslope at an almost imperceptible rate. Whereas the results of free fall and landslides are immediately and conspicuously apparent, the effects of much soil creep are detectable only after measurements have been carried out over many years or decades. Soil creep in climatically harsh regions with *permafrost* (permanently frozen subsoil or bedrock) is called *gelifluction* (also *solifluction*). This may involve the downslope flowage of sheets of saturated surficial debris at rates approaching a foot or more per year. Creep in warmer regions tends to occur much more slowly; its effects are often discovered accidentally or only indirectly, since it operates, generally, at such a slow rate as scarcely to be noticeable on a year-to-year basis.

All of the types of mass movement have been — and are today — active in southern Alberta. Undoubtedly the most outstanding case of gravity in action as an agent of gradation is the internationally known Frank Slide, a classic example of a landslide of the rock fall variety. However, smaller, less spectacular mass movement forms abound in the region, and over the course of geologic time these have probably been more important in landscape evolution than has been the dramatic, but only occasional, event.

Figure 3. Composite landslide along old Highway 3, West Lethbridge. The toe and much of the middle part of this slide flowed, while the upper part (arrow) sustained mainly slump.

Summary

Evolution of the landscapes of southern Alberta has been dependent upon operation of all of the agents of gradation, although the contribution of waves and currents has been minimal. Comparative intensity of each of the agents has varied from place to place and time to time, and the geomorphologic character of any particular part of the larger area tends, in the main, to reflect the operation of those agents most recently active. Running water, the wind, the ubiquitous effect of gravity, glacial ice in the mountains and on the plains — all have cut, carved, transported, and rearranged the surficial earth materials of our part of North America.

However, before discussing the larger and smaller landscape elements of this diversified region, it is useful to think a little bit about the fundamental geologic framework on and in which the gradational forces have acted. A detailed, technical account is not necessary for our purposes, but some uncomplicated geologic facts will help.

CHAPTER 2
THE GEOLOGIC FOUNDATION

The basic geology of much of southern Alberta is relatively simple. This is especially the case in the plains, where bedrock to depths of thousands of feet consists primarily of sedimentary rocks, mainly sandstones and shales, arranged in horizontal or nearly horizontal layers. Conditions become somewhat more disorderly in the foothills and mountains, but the overall geologic pattern is not difficult to grasp.

Rock Types

Rocks are the primary stuff of geology, the substance of most of the earth's crust and the skeleton, so to speak, of all surficial forms. The geologist is interested in a great many characteristics of rocks — what they are made of, how they were formed, how they differ from place to place, what has happened to them after formation, and what resources they may contain, to list but a few. Our concern will be mainly with (1) types of rock, (2) what each kind suggests in terms of origin, and (3) how they are distributed in southern Alberta.

The system of rock classification outlined here has been used internationally for more than 100 years and is based on origin — the three fundamental categories are *genetic*. These are *igneous, sedimentary,* and *metamorphic (Table I)*. Each term refers to a group of rocks of perhaps dissimilar appearance and chemical or mineralogic makeup, but all of which have shared a common mode of formation. Table I contains the names and brief descriptions of some of the more common rock types present in the earth's crust.

Igneous rocks have been formed by the solidification of molten rock material, or *magma*; magma which reaches the earth's surface is known as *lava*. There are two basic types of igneous rocks: (1) Those which have cooled and hardened deep within the crust of the earth, the *intrusive* or *plutonic* rocks, and (2) those which have solidified at or near the surface, the *extrusive* or *volcanic* rocks. The place of cooling and solidifying is important in determining the physical appearance of an igneous rock. The extrusive rocks (the lavas) have cooled very quickly and tend to be fine-grained, the most extreme example being the natural glass *obsidian,* which completely lacks a recognizable crystalline structure. In contrast, the intrusive or plutonic rocks have cooled slowly at depths of several miles, with the formation of comparatively large, interlocking crystals. Such rocks tend to be relatively coarse-grained, the individual mineral constituents being readily visible to the naked eye. The appearance of an igneous rock, whether it is coarse- or fine-grained, is thus an important potential clue to its place of origin and may shed considerable light on the geologic history of the area in which it is found.

Many *sedimentary rocks* are made up of fragmental materials — mineral, organic (plant materials or shell), or pieces of pre-existent rock — that have been transported by one or more of the agents of gradation to a settling basin in which accumulation of individual beds can take place. Some sedimentary rocks are of *chemical* origin, consisting almost entirely of mineral matter that has been precipitated from solution. But virtually all sedimentary rocks share one most significant characteristic: They are layered, or *stratified,* arranged in successive beds of accumulation one on top of the other. If a sequence of such beds has not been disturbed, obviously the one at the bottom is the oldest, with increasingly younger layers on top of it. This reasonably self-evident relationship is known to geologists as the *Principle of Superposition,* and in spite of its seeming simplicity, it has proved to be one of the most useful generalizations applied by earth scientists to geologic problems. For historical geologists in particular, the sedimentary rocks have been all but indispensible, since almost all of the fossils yet discovered have been found in such rocks. Volumetrically the sedimentary rocks make up only a relatively small fraction of the crust of the earth. However, their areal extent is considerable (they are at the surface over some 70-75 percent of the continents), and their importance to the science of geology is difficult to overemphasize.

The *metamorphic rocks* are pre-existent rocks of one sort or another that have been changed (metamorphosed) as a result of the application of heat, pressure, or both. Additionally, some metamorphic rocks appear to have originated through complex chemical reactions generated by the movement of hot, reactive fluids through volumes of pre-existent rock. Geologists believe that most metamorphic processes occur in rock material that remains solid; the mineral

TABLE I — ROCK TYPES

Category and Name	Description	Category and Name	Description
IGNEOUS		**SEDIMENTARY**	
		Conglomerate	Cemented gravel, made up of rounded pebbles in a matrix of finer material.
Intrusive			
Granite	Light-colored, pinkish to grey, medium- to coarse-grained. A very common igneous rock in many of the world's mountain ranges.	Sandstone	Sand-sized particles cemented together by *calcite, silica,* or an *iron oxide.*
Quartz Diorite	Medium-to-dark grey granular rock of medium to coarse grain size. Intermediate in mineralogic composition between *granite* and *gabbro.*	Shale	Hardened, cemented silts and clays; very fine-grained. Variations are known as *siltstone* and *mudstone.*
Gabbro	Dark colored, medium to coarse grained rock high in minerals with *iron* and *magnesium.*	Limestone	Consists of calcium carbonate, $CaCO_3$ or *calcite.* May be fragmental or precipitated from solution.
Peridotite	Dull green igneous rock made up largely of the minerals *olivene* and *pyroxene.*	Dolomite	A *carbonate* rock consisting of the mineral *dolomite,* $CaMg(CO_3)_2$. Also known as *dolostone.*
		METAMORPHIC	
		Foliated (layered)	
		Slate	Fine-grained, brittle rock that splits easily into thin layers. Still used as roofing in parts of the world.
Extrusive		Schist	Foliated rock often made up of thin mineral particles, especially tiny sheets of *mica.*
Basalt	Black to medium grey, fine-grained rock. The extrusive equivalent of *gabbro.* Most common of the volcanic rocks, or *lavas.*	Gneiss	Medium to coarse grained rock, usually consisting of alternating layers of dark and light colored minerals.
Andesite	Darkish or greenish grey in color; fine-grained. Widespread in the *Andes Mountains* in South America, hence its name.	**Massive** (non-foliated)	
Rhyolite	Fine-grained, light colored rock. The extrusive equivalent of *granite.* May be banded or streaked out by flowage.	Quartzite	Metamorphosed quartz sandstone, generally light-colored. Very hard, resistant rock, probably toughest of all.
Obsidian	Black, brown, or reddish glassy rock lacking recognizable crystalline structure. Thin pieces are often transparent. Used for tools.	Marble	Recrystallized limestone, consisting of interlocked crystals of calcite. Many varieties and colors.
		Argillite	A fairly tough, compact rock consisting of recrystallized mudstone or siltstone.

constituents are physically rearranged or may undergo sequences of chemical exchange and replacement, but melting does not occur. Such processes are possible only at considerable depths within the earth's crust where the required conditions of high temperature and pressure are encountered. Accordingly, the presence of a metamorphic rock at the earth's surface carries with it certain significant implications: A pre-existent rock must have been buried to a considerable depth within the crust, subjected to the necessary heat, pressure, or permeation by chemically active fluids, and then exposed by uplift and erosional removal of perhaps several miles of overburden. Every metamorphic rock has thus experienced a complex developmental history. Since geologists have never been able to observe first-hand the formation of metamorphic rocks (whereas the origin of some igneous and sedimentary rocks can be watched directly in the natural world), such rocks have long presented an intellectual and physical challenge to earth scientists.

This all too brief introduction to *petrology* (the branch of geology dealing with the origin, occurrence, structure, and history of rocks) will serve to suggest at least some of the topics and problems of interest to those geologists most directly concerned with the materials of the earth's crust and surface. The rock types of southern Alberta are not many, but their physical characteristics, areal distribution, and structural features are of importance to an understanding of landscape history in this part of the province.

Tectonic Processes

Mention has been made of the *internal* or *tectonic* processes which affect the surface of the earth. In general, these function to elevate parts of the crust, to create relief in direct opposition to the operation of the gradational forces. Energy to drive the tectonic forces is generated internally; most geologists and geophysicists believe that this energy is related in one way or another to the release of heat by internal processes of radioactivity.

As noted earlier, tectonic processes are divided into two broad classes, *vulcanism* and *diastrophism.* The distinction is based upon fundamental differences in types of activity and on observable processes at the earth's surface. *Vulcanism* involves relief creation by the addition of new material — by volcanic activity — and may proceed relatively violently (*explosive vulcanism*) or comparatively quietly (*effusive vulcanism*). Explosive vulcanism builds *cinder cones.* These are roughly symmetrical piles of fragmental rock debris

(*pyroclastic* — literally "fire-broken" — material) that accumulate around the vents from which liquid and solidified lavas are ejected. Effusive vulcanism, in contrast, depends upon the generally non-explosive outpouring of great volumes of very fluid lava from one or more vents or conduits which spreads laterally to build massive, low-sloping cones of rock known as *shield volcanoes.* The Hawaiian Islands, for example, consist of a 1,000-mile chain of enormous shield volcanoes, only the upper parts of which are above sea level.

A combination of alternating explosive and effusive volcanic episodes from a single vent or from two or three closely spaced vents results in the formation of high, symmetrical cones known as *strato-volcanoes* (also, *composite volcanoes*). Most of the well-known volcanic peaks of the earth (Etna in Sicily, Fujiyama in Japan, Ranier, Hood, and Shasta in the Cascades of Washington, Oregon, and California) are of this type. Their symmetry and perfection of shape are simply a reflection of their youthfulness; the erosive processes have made little impact on the tectonically produced forms.

Volcanic activity is responsible for other larger and smaller tectonic features. In some parts of the earth, great thicknesses of layered lavas have accumulated to form *lava fields* or *lava plateaus.* Much of the interior American Pacific Northwest is known as the Columbia Plateau; here, many tens of individual sheets of lava have piled up to thicknesses exceeding several thousand feet, completely burying a fairly rugged non-volcanic landscape, only bits and pieces of which can now be seen in the walls of the larger river canyons. Parts of south-central British Columbia also are characterized by extensive masses of layered volcanic rocks.

On a much smaller scale, thin, sheet-like masses of fluid rock material may penetrate fractures or other zones of weakness in a mass of rock near the surface to solidify as *dikes* (which cut *across* beds of sediment at a high angle) or *sills* (which *parallel* the bedding in a sequence of sedimentary rocks).

The variety of types of vulcanism is great, and many parts of the earth's surface — but *not* including southern Alberta — have landscapes dominated by the forms of volcanic activity.

Diastrophism, the second of the tectonic processes, is the creation of surficial relief without the addition of new material. Diastrophism may be relatively localized in its operation and effects, in which case it is known as *orogeny* (literally, mountain origin or mountain building), or it may affect areas of sub-continental or even continental size, in which case the term *epeirogeny* is applied (from the Greek *epeiros*: continent or mainland + genesis). As noted earlier, although volcanic activity is undeniably more violent and spectacular, diastrophic processes appear to have been much more important in shaping the surface features of the greater part of the crust throughout earth history.

Figure 4. Folded sedimentary rocks in Waterton Lakes National Park. This exposure is on the west side of the road just north of the Cameron Lake junction.

Diastrophic forces produce distortion or dislocation of segments of the crust in a number of ways. Probably the most readily recognizable is *folding,* the bending of rocks into wave-like crenulations *(Figure 4).* Most rocks at the surface of the earth seem to be rigid and unyielding, and the idea that they could be warped or folded into simple or intricate structures may strike many of us as quite preposterous. Yet at depth within the earth's crust, in a high-pressure, high-temperature environment, many rocks will yield plastically to long-sustained stresses, deforming into wave-like folded structures from layers initially horizontal. Many geologists think that folding, simple or complex, is the result of compressive stresses exerted more or less horizontally; folding, in short, suggests (but does not in itself *prove*) that a shortening of part of the crust has occurred. An elaborate

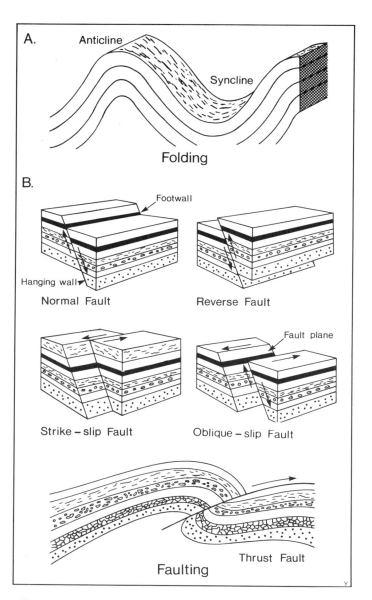

Figure 5. Simplified diagrams showing types of tectonic deformation in rocks of the earth's crust. A. Folding; B. Faulting.

terminology has been developed to describe the geometry of folding, but for our purposes only two terms will suffice: Masses of rock which have been downbent or downfolded are called *synclines,* while those that have been upfolded are known as *anticlines (Figure 5).* Synclinal and anticlinal folding are very common in the rocks of the crust and may range in scale from features a few inches in length to mountain-size structures.

Under certain circumstances (and these are not yet completely understood), rocks subjected to deforming pressures will break or fracture along surfaces of separation, rather than yielding plastically to form folds. Such offset fractures or breaks in solid rock are labeled *faults;* faulting is thus another form of diastrophic activity *(see Figure 5). Normal* or *gravity faulting* occurs when a slab of crustal material is subjected to tensional forces and one block moves *down* relative to another; such faulting is thus believed to be an indication of a stretching or extension of a part of the crust. *Reverse faulting* occurs when, in response to compressive forces, one piece of crust moves *up* along the surface of faulting (the *fault plane*) relative to an adjacent piece *(Figure 6).* As illustrated in *Figure 5,* the expressions *hanging wall* and *footwall* are often encountered in descriptions of faulting. These are mining terms and refer to surfaces of blocks of rock *above* (the hanging wall) and *below* (the footwall) a tunnel excavated along a sloping body of ore or coal. Thus, in a so-called normal fault, the hanging wall block moves *down* relative to the footwall block, whereas in a reverse fault the opposite movement occurs. Reverse faults of very low inclination are spoken of as *thrust* or *overthurst faults,* since in these the rocks of the hanging wall block are literally thrust considerable distances *over* those of the footwall block. Faulting of this sort has been widespread in the Alberta foothills and mountains.

With the exception of overthrusting, the faulting described above involves mainly vertical movements of chunks of crust. Other kinds of movement are possible, of course. *Strike-slip,* or *transcurrent, faults* are those in which movement by one block relative to another block along the surface trace (or *strike*) of the fault plane is predominantly horizontal. The well-known *San Andreas* fault of California is of this type, for example. In still another variation, some faulting involves both horizontal and vertical movement, in which case the term *oblique-slip faulting* is appropriate. Whatever the nature of the movement, however, faulting is simply another indication of the application of stresses (pressures) to blocks of the crust by internally produced forces. The steady generation of internal energy by the release of radioactive heat has made the earth a geologically restless planet throughout most of its history.

Folding and faulting are readily recognizable manifestations of orogenic activity. Evidence for earth movements of an *epeirogenic* nature is less directly observable than that described above, but there can be little doubt about the reality of large-scale vertical and tilting movements (both up and down) of sizable pieces of crust. In many parts of the earth,

Figure 6. Small reverse fault (arrow) in rocks exposed in the St. Mary River valley south of Lethbridge. The darker colored beds are thin seams of coal. Total offset in this fault is about 4-5 feet.

great thicknesses of horizontally bedded *marine* sedimentary rocks (known to have formed in a marine, or oceanic, environment by virtue of their fossils) are situated today at elevations thousands of feet above sea level. They simply couldn't have formed in their present locations, yet they are found in an essentially undeformed condition high above the required environment of origin. Only broad, large-scale uplift of pieces of crust of sub-continental size could account for the presence of such rocks in their present locations. In North America, one of the better examples of the effects of this kind of tectonic activity is represented by the Colorado Plateau country of the American southwest, where thousands of feet of such sediments are exposed at elevations of 6,000 to 8,000 feet in the walls of the Grand Canyon of the Colorado River and its larger and smaller tributaries.

In the same manner, although in a somewhat less spectacular setting, many of the nearly horizontal sedimentary rocks of the southern Alberta plains are also marine in origin, yet today they are more than 2,000-3,000 feet above sea level and still have undergone only minor deformation. Widespread evidence of this sort, indirect though it may be, points clearly to the effectiveness of epeirogeny.

A final point about the tectonic processes should be stressed. We have a pretty good idea of the rates at which various high-standing parts of the earth's surface are being worn down by action of the gradational processes. Although these may seem quite insignificant by human standards (a few inches per thousand years, for example), erosional lowering at even the slowest rate would reduce most of the continents to broad, flat plains at or only slightly above sea level in a comparatively short finite time, say a matter of a few hundred million years. Radiometric dating indicates that the age of the earth is about 4.5 *billion* years. Obviously, time, and time enough, has elapsed during earth history for many generations of high-standing continents to have been completely eroded away. Yet the geologic evidence suggests that the continents of the present are as high as, or perhaps even higher than, they have ever been over the past two or three billion years.

One conclusion seems inescapable: Intensities and rates of operation of the tectonic processes generally have kept pace with those of the gradational processes. Otherwise, the continents would long ago have been worn down to broad, featureless, sea-level plains. Although there are very real dangers of waxing overly poetic about the matter, it is certainly correct to think of the history of the surface of the earth as being directly controlled by the never-ending struggle or contest between the internal (tectonic) and external (gradational) forces and processes. Forces of uplift have been opposed by forces of degradation; one or the other has temporarily held the upper hand at various times and places, but a rough balance must have been maintained, on a world-wide scale, throughout most of earth history.

The Southern Alberta Scene

In terms of structure and variety of rock types present, how can the region of interest to this volume be characterized? A simplified cross-sectional sketch *(Figure 7)* will serve to illustrate the major structural features. As already noted, the plains of southern Alberta are underlain dominantly by sedimentary rocks of more or less horizontal attitude. Two large but gentle subsurface structures, the northern extension of the Sweetgrass Arch (a broad anticline best developed in Montana) and the Alberta Syncline, impart dips of a few to a few tens of feet per mile to bedrock underlying the plains, but these structures are not conspicuously reflected by surface forms.

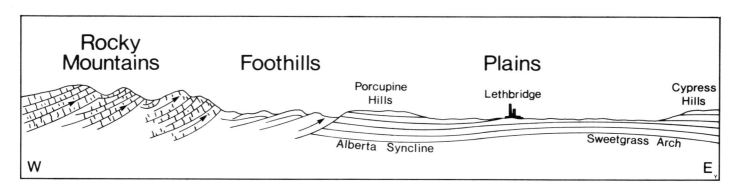

Figure 7. Simplified cross-sectional sketch of southern Alberta showing the basic structural features of this part of the province. The vertical dimension is greatly exaggerated.

Structural conditions become more complex as the eastern margin of the Rockies is approached. The Foothills Belt consists of an elongated zone of folded and thrust-faulted beds, roughly paralleling the mountain front in their northwest-southeast alignment. Here, there is often a fairly direct relationship between underlying structure and surface topography, in that upfolded or upfaulted rocks underlie many of the linear ridges. The rocks of the Foothills Belt are generally of the same type and age as those of the plains, mainly marine and continental sandstones and shales. The structural characteristics of the foothills appear to be the result of an easterly extension of powerful forces exerted in formation of the Rockies farther west.

The main linear ranges of the southern Alberta Rockies (the Livingstone, Blairmore, Highwood, Clark, High Rock, and Flathead ranges, and others) consist fundamentally of great slabs of older sedimentary rocks that have been moved considerable distances to the east or northeast along numerous low-angle thrust faults. Total horizontal movement on some of the major faults has been as much as several tens of miles. In many places, older rocks have been thrust above younger formations, thus reversing the normal stratigraphic relationship (the youngest beds are usually at the *top* in an accumulation of layered sediments). In the extreme southwestern part of the province, ancient rocks of Precambrian age (known as the *Purcell System* in Alberta and British Columbia and the *Belt Series* in Montana) have been shoved easterly and northeasterly over younger formations along the *Lewis Thrust*, a major thrust fault in both the Canadian and American Rockies.

There is no general agreement among geologists as to just how or why the elongated blocks of the Rocky Mountain ranges were moved toward the east. As the structural characteristics of the region became known early in this century, it was first postulated that some unspecified force from the west must have pushed the slabs of limestone, sandstone, and siltstone in an easterly direction. More recently, some earth scientists have concluded that simple pushing from the west is a highly improbable physical process. Instead, they propose the mechanism of *gravity sliding* to account for the undoubted easterly movements. In this model, it is assumed that a broad crustal arch formed to the west of the Rockies and that great sheets of sedimentary rocks, lubricated by interstitial water and aided by failure along weaker beds, literally slid down its gentle eastern slope, overriding younger formations as they moved. Details of the supposed process are obscure, but to many geologists it seems to offer a more feasible explanation for the observed structural features of the region than does the simple "push" model of earlier times. As is the case with so many fundamental problems of earth history, this one has not yet been satisfactorily resolved.

The different rock types of southern Alberta are most conveniently represented by means of idealized, generalized sections showing all rocks present from oldest to youngest *(Table II-A and II-B)*. At no single locality within the larger region are *all* of the various types found together; the sections simply display, in readily understandable fashion, the diversity

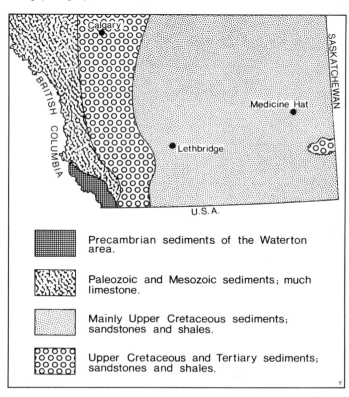

Precambrian sediments of the Waterton area.

Paleozoic and Mesozoic sediments; much limestone.

Mainly Upper Cretaceous sediments; sandstones and shales.

Upper Cretaceous and Tertiary sediments; sandstones and shales.

Figure 8. Simplified geologic map of southern Alberta showing generalized distribution of major groups of rocks by age and type. Bedrock in most of the plains is overlain by glacial debris of variable thickness.

TABLE II

A. SOUTHERN ALBERTA FOOTHILLS AND MOUNTAINS

Geologic Age			Names of Formations	General Characteristics
CENOZOIC	Quaternary	Recent		Modern soils, stream sands and gravels, slope deposits
		Pleistocene		Till, outwash, lake bed sediments, interglacial stream deposits
	Tertiary	Paleocene	Porcupine Hills	Sandstone, shale
MESOZOIC		Upper Cretaceous	Willow Creek	Sandstone, shale, mudstone
			St. Mary River	Sandstone, shale
			Blood Reserve	Sandstone, shale
			Belly River	Sandstone, mudstone, shale, *coal seams*
			Wapiabi	Shale, siltstone
			Cardium	Sandstone, siltstone, shale
			Blackstone	Shale, siltstone
		Lower Cretaceous	Crowsnest volcanics	Fragmental volcanic materials
			Blairmore	Sandstone, shale, conglomerate
			Kootenay	Sandstone, shale, *coal seams*
		Jurassic	Kootenay	Sandstone, shale, *coal seams*
			Fernie	Sandstone, shale, limestone
		Triassic	Several formations	Dolomite, sandstone, siltstone
PALEOZOIC		Permian	Several formations	Quartzitic sandstone, siltstone
		Pennsylvanian	Several formations	Dolomite, sandstone, siltstone
		Mississippian	Several formations	Limestone, dolomite, shales. Rocks of *Frank Slide* come from this group
		Devonian	Several formations	Mainly limestone and dolomite
		Cambrian	Several formations	Limestone, dolomite, sandstone, shale, siltstone
PRE-CAMBRIAN		Upper	Rocks of the *Purcell System;* various formational names	Argillite, dolomite, limestone, quartzite, *Purcell Lava*
		Lower	"Basement"; presumably a buried extension of the Canadian Shield	Crystalline igneous and metamorphic rocks

GENERALIZED GEOLOGIC SECTIONS

B. SOUTHERN ALBERTA PLAINS

Geologic Age			Names of Formations	General Characteristics
CENOZOIC	Quaternary	Recent		Modern soils, loess, stream sands and gravels, slope deposits
		Pleistocene		Till, outwash, lake bed sediments, interglacial stream deposits
	Tertiary	Pliocene (?)		Sandstone
		Oligocene	Cypress Hills	Conglomerate — gravels
		Paleocene	Ravenscrag	Sandstones
			Porcupine Hills	Sandstones, shales
			Willow Creek	Shales, sandstones, clays
MESOZOIC	Upper Cretaceous		Whitemud	Mainly clays, sandstone at base
			St. Mary River	Sandstones, shales
			Blood Reserve	Sandstones
			Bearpaw	Mainly dark shales
			Oldman	Shales, sandstones, *coal seams, dinosaur fossils*
			Foremost	Sandstones, shales, *coal seams*
			Pakowki	Mainly shales
			Milk River	Mainly sandstones, *ironstone concretions*
			Alberta	Mainly shales
	Lower Cretaceous		(Blairmore-Kootenay?)	Greenish and reddish shales
	Jurassic			Mostly shales, some limestones and sandstones
PALEOZOIC	Mississippian			Limestones
	Devonian			Limestones
	Cambrian			Limestones and dolomites, some shales
PRE-CAMBRIAN			"Basement"; buried extension of Canadian Shield	Crystalline metamorphic and igneous rocks

TABLE III
STANDARDIZED
GEOLOGIC COLUMN AND TIME SCALE

Era	Period	Epoch	Significant Life Events	Duration (Million Years)*	Million Years Ago*
CENOZOIC	Quaternary	Recent / Pleistocene	Rise of man	2-3	
	Tertiary	Pliocene	Abundance and great variety of mammals	10	
		Miocene		14	
		Oligocene	Rise of mammals; first horses	11	
		Eocene		16	
		Paleocene		12	65
MESOZOIC	Cretaceous		Last dinosaurs and ammonites; first flowering plants	71	
	Jurassic		First birds and mammals; abundant ammonites	54	
	Triassic		First dinosaurs	35	225
PALEOZOIC	Permian		First conifers; last trilobites; many invertebrates die out	55	
	Pennsylvanian		Abundant swamps — coal; insects, amphibians	40	
	Mississippian		First reptiles?	25	
	Devonian		First trees and amphibians; abundance of fish	50	
	Silurian		First land plants? Coral reefs	35	
	Ordovician		First fish	70	
	Cambrian		First really abundant fossils; many trilobites	70	570
PRECAMBRIAN	Upper Proterozoic		Primitive invertebrates — sponges, worms, algae, bacteria, and others	300	
	Middle Proterozoic			700	
	Lower Proterozoic			800	2400
	Archeozoic		Rare algae and bacteria?	2100	

Origin of earth about 4500 million years ago

*Approximate ages based on recent radiometric dating.

of formations recognized to date. *Table III* is the standardized Geologic Column and Time Table; this indicates the names and approximate ages (determined by fossils and radiometric dating) of the larger units of geologic time recognized by geologists around the world.

As the tables suggest, southern Alberta can be divided into two major rock-type regions. The *plains and Foothills Belt* are underlain primarily by sedimentary rocks of Cretaceous age and younger, veneered in most places by unconsolidated glacial and post-glacial deposits. The *Rockies* (technically known as the *Front Ranges* in southwestern Alberta), consist of great linear ranges of limestones, dolomites, sandstones, and siltstones (and some metamorphic equivalents), largely of Paleozoic age, but including the sedimentary rocks of the Precambrian Purcell System in the extreme southwest. A simplified geologic map of the area is shown in *Figure 8*.

Conspicuously absent as outcrops at the surface in most parts of southern Alberta are igneous rocks. However, east and west of Coleman is a linear north-south zone of extrusive igneous rocks, the *Crowsnest Volcanics* (of Cretaceous age). And sandwiched within the Precambrian sediments of the southern Rockies are a sill of dark-colored igneous material and a 200-foot layer of dark green basalt (the *Purcell Lava*), both of which are noticeable in places because of their color contrast with the lighter sedimentary units. Otherwise, the closest igneous rocks are thousands of feet below the surface in the so-called crystalline "basement", a buried extension of the Canadian Shield made up largely of ancient (Precambrian)

igneous and metamorphic formations. An exception to this latter statement is represented by *Black Butte* in southeastern Alberta and the *Sweetgrass Hills* of Montana, which will be briefly discussed in the chapter on the plains.

The geological "raw materials" on which gradational processes have operated to create the landscapes of southern Alberta are thus largely sedimentary rocks, varying in age from Precambrian to late Cenozoic. In the plains, the structure of such rocks is comparatively simple on a regional scale, and the gross characteristics of the topography generally reflect this simplicity. Tectonic activity in the form of faulting, folding, and broad, regional uplift has created a much more complex situation in the foothills and mountains. Gradational processes there have functioned in an area of considerable structural relief, and the diversity of land forms is rather directly dependent upon the variety of structural features.

The material presented in this and the preceding chapter is intended to serve as a useful background to what follows. The plan is to discuss the three major physiographic regions of southern Alberta — the Rockies, the Foothills Belt, and the plains — in that order. Each will be described in terms of its basic geological framework, operation of the gradational forces, and the particular suite of land forms resulting from the interplay of the various opposing and complementary processes. Geomorphologic features of unique or special interest will be noted where deemed appropriate, but the major emphasis will be on the general, overall character of each of the contrasting landscapes.

* * * * *

CHAPTER 3
THE ROCKIES

Two geomorphological characteristics are especially prominent in many parts of the Rocky Mountain region: (1) Large areas have exceptionally steep slopes with little or no soil or vegetation cover, so that structural features, particularly layering or bedding, are easily seen; and (2) in marked contrast to the foothills and plains, relief is great, amounting typically to several thousand feet. These landscape characteristics are not, of course, restricted only to the Rockies of southern Alberta, since they are evident in most of the high ranges in western North America and elsewhere in the world, but they certainly give to the mountains an appearance notably different from that of other parts of the region.

In the main, Rocky Mountain geomorphology is a reflection of extensive alpine glaciation operating in a tectonically produced structural landscape. Post-glacial gradational activity has in many places only slightly modified land forms left behind as the most recent glaciers stagnated and wasted away. An understanding of the landscape is thus dependent upon an appreciation of the basic geology, coupled with knowledge of how alpine glaciers function to build their own distinctive set of land forms.

Structural Characteristics

Geologists have wrestled with the structural complexities of the Rocky Mountain province for more than 100 years. The Alberta Rockies were first observed by scientific eyes in the 1850's, when Dr. James Hector, physician-geologist of the Palliser expedition, made several crossings of the southern segment and noted the more conspicuous elements of the geomorphology, including the elongated blocks of tilted sedimentary rocks that constitute the linear Front Ranges. Since that time, the intensity and sophistication of geological investigation have steadily increased, with both theoretical and applied goals in mind, so that today we are in a position to discuss with some degree of confidence the larger structural features that account for the major topographic subdivisions.

A very generalized description of Rocky Mountain structure was given in the last chapter. As indicated there, the dominant elements of the landscape are great slabs of sedimentary rocks that have been tilted, folded, and moved many miles to the east or northeast along low-angle thrust faults. Geologists postulate that tilting, faulting, and folding operated intermittently during Mesozoic and Cenozoic time;

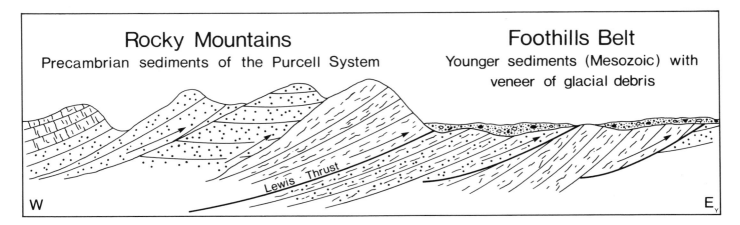

Figure 9. Structural conditions along the Rocky Mountain front in northern Waterton Lakes National Park. The cross-section is simplified somewhat, but the basic structural features are correctly shown.

Figure 10. Rocky Mountain front in Waterton Lakes National Park. The picture was taken from the viewpoint at the Buffalo Paddock turnoff.

the most recent episode of tectonic activity seems to have involved regional uplift amounting to thousands of feet in most of the Rocky Mountain province and produced the beginnings of the modern mountains perhaps three or four million years ago. The precise mechanism of movement on the thrust faults is unknown, and, as suggested earlier, there is dispute among earth scientists concerning the matter. For our purposes, the *results* of the movement are more important than specific details of the process itself, and these results are readily apparent in the landscape.

A somewhat simplified structural cross-section of the Rockies in northern Waterton Lakes National Park is given in *Figure 9,* and a photograph of the mountain front in this area is shown in *Figure 10.* The Lewis Thrust, described in the

preceding chapter, approximately defines the base of the mountains. Above this major thrust fault, and constituting the bulk of the range, are sedimentary rocks of Precambrian age, formations belonging to the Purcell System. The lower terrain in the foreground of Figure 10 is veneered with glacial debris and underlain by sandstones and shales of Cretaceous age. These younger bedrock formations, which extend beneath the Lewis Thrust along the mountain front, are part of the Foothills Belt and are also cut in places by westward-dipping thrust faults. The structural pattern here is clear: Older rocks have been moved eastward over younger rocks, and the great slab of layered Precambrian sediments above the Lewis Thrust represents the first, or easternmost, of the Front Ranges in this part of the province.

With variations, this basic structural theme is found throughout most of the Rocky Mountains of southwestern Alberta. As one moves north from the international boundary, the age and type of rocks change, but the pattern of eastward thrusting of thick masses of sediments is repeated. Thus, north of Highway 3 through Crowsnest Pass the imposing front of the High Rock Range towers above the adjacent valley to the

Figure 11. Southern end of the High Rock Range as seen from above Crowsnest Lake.

east *(Figure 11)*, with the Lewis Thrust again underlying the eastern flank of the range. Here, the tilted limestones of the mountains are of Middle and Upper Paleozoic age, but the general structural conditions so well displayed near Waterton Park are essentially duplicated.

Similarly, the steep, straight eastern face of the Livingstone Range is the eroded edge of a thick sequence of Paleozoic limestones thrust to the east along the Livingstone Fault and overlying sandstones and shales of younger age *(Figure 12)*. The details may differ from place to place, but the *general* structural pattern within the Rockies shows the linear ranges to be masses of Paleozoic sediments (mostly grey limestones) thrust eastward along low-angle faults, with the valleys usually underlain by younger rocks.

Of particular structural (and scenic) interest is Crowsnest Mountain, shown in *Figure 13*. This prominent summit is what is known to geologists as a *klippe,* an isolated remnant of the same rock types that make up the High Rock Range to the west. The Lewis Thrust, along which Crowsnest Mountain and the High Rock Range have moved to the east, passes through the former at roughly the upper limit of the trees; rocks above the fault are Paleozoic limestones, while those below are sandstones and shales of Cretaceous age. Crowsnest Mountain has been physiographically detached from the High Rock Range by erosional removal of a large mass of once-contiguous rock. Formation of the valley of Allison Creek resulted in isolation of the mountain, leaving the structural situation sketched in *Figure 14.*

Figure 12. Eastern flank of the southern Livingstone Range. Centre Peak is the high point on the right side of the skyline.

Farther south, Chief Mountain in northeastern Glacier National Park *(Figure 15)* is of the same structural type — the upper part of the mountain consists of Precambrian rocks (part of the Belt Series) which overlie younger sediments beneath the Lewis Thrust, the whole massif separated from the main body of the Rockies by gradational removal of a once-continuous volume of rock.

It should be stressed that the *detailed* structural characteristics of any given part of the Alberta Rockies may be (and often are) extremely complex. Intensive exploration by the oil industry has revealed the existence of structural features, particularly intricate patterns of folding complicated by faulting, an understanding of which taxes the ingenuity of even the most talented and imaginative geologists. But such structural complexities are not of immediate concern in the present context. The larger elements of the Front Ranges province — the generally linear, tilted masses of sedimentary rocks and the intervening valleys — have been created, in the main, by thrust-faulting from the west and southwest on a massive scale. Even without the valley-deepening effects of erosion by running water and glacial ice, much of the Rocky Mountain landscape would presumably be fairly rugged and possessed of considerable relief; the basic geological framework assures that this would be the case.

Gradation in the Mountains

Three of the agents of gradation have been — and two are today — responsible for most alteration of tectonically produced forms leading to the landscapes of the present. *Running water, glacial ice,* and *gravity* have functioned throughout the mountains as forces of change, all operating over tens of millions of years to reduce relief and, given sufficient time and tectonic standstill, to destroy the Rockies.

There is no reason to believe that before glaciation enveloped the Alberta Front Ranges the actions of two of the gradational agents — running water and gravity — were significantly different from what they are at present. That is to say, streams east of the Continental Divide must have organized their flow into integrated drainage systems leading toward and onto the plains, and the effects of gravity undoubtedly produced mass movements much as we observe today. It is highly probable that all of the modern rivers — the Kananaskis, Elbow, Sheep, Highwood, Livingstone, Oldman, Crowsnest, Carbondale, and Castle — were in approximately the locations we find them currently occupying. The same was very likely true of the smaller stream systems, including those that collectively give rise to the Waterton, Belly, and St. Mary rivers. This is just another way of noting that the overall pattern of ridges and valleys within the mountains was not greatly unlike that of the present immediately prior to glaciation.

But there must have been differences, as well. Before formation of extensive glaciers, the general appearance of the landscape was probably more rounded and subdued than it is

Figure 13. Crowsnest Mountain as seen from slightly west of south. Crowsnest Lake is in the middle ground.

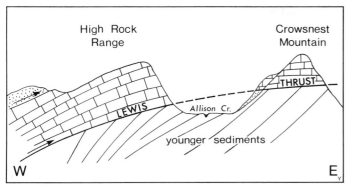

Figure 14. Structural conditions at Crowsnest Mountain. The mountain was once part of the great slab of limestone making up the High Rock Range to the west, but has been isolated by formation of the valley of Allison Creek.

at present, with less relief, far fewer steep, bedrock slopes, and perhaps a more complete forest cover. Running water then conformed to the same physical laws that govern its contemporary behavior. That is, erosion, transportation, and deposition of fragmental debris were accomplished by the pre-glacial streams and rivers, with rock and mineral material destined finally to be carried out of the mountains. Similarly, landslides and other less conspicuous forms of mass movement must have caused transformations of terrain, with all processes of gradation operating to wear down the high-standing units of the landscape, to reduce general relief.

Then came widespread glaciation. It is worth mentioning that in spite of nearly 200 years of study of the *effects* of glacial action, there is still no general agreement among the "experts" about *causes*. Explanations have ranged from the bizarre and catastrophic to the subtle and scarcely comprehensible, but the fact of the matter is that no single, ultimate cause (or combination of causes) has yet been satisfactorily identified, at least not to the satisfaction of all interested parties.

The basic requirement for initiation of glaciation is ridiculously simple: More snow must fall and accumulate during the winter than is lost in the following summer to melting and other processes that reduce volume; collectively, such volume-reducing processes are known as *ablation*. So long as accumulation exceeds ablation, on a year-to-year or decade-by-decade basis, volumes will increase, the transformation of light, fluffy snow to hard, crystalline ice will take place, and *voila* — an ice age may have begun! However,

having made note of this fairly obvious relationship, one really hasn't advanced very far toward the discovery of possible causes. These have been grouped into two large classes: (1) Those related to events or changing conditions on the earth's surface or in its atmosphere, the *terrestrial* causes; and (2) those related to events outside the planet and its atmosphere, the non-terrestrial or *astronomic* causes. A third category, favored by many investigators, includes a combination of both terrestrial and astronomic factors.

This is not the place and the author is certainly not the person to attempt a complete explanation of the cause (or causes) of glaciation. Suffice it to state that many meteorologists believe quite significant climatological effects could be produced in time by very small initial changes in atmospheric composition or circulation, location of the continents on the surface of the earth, elevation of certain mountain ranges, position of the earth in the solar system, or radiational output of the Sun. The geologic record indicates that glaciation of the magnitude of that of the last 2-3 million years (the period of time known as the Pleistocene) has been relatively rare in earth history. Whatever the cause or combination of causes may be, the "normal" condition of our planet appears not to have included massive continental and

Figure 15. Chief Mountain as seen from near Police Outpost Provincial Park.

alpine glaciers. The Pleistocene Epoch — the so-called Ice Age — was thus a very special time in earth history, and the landscape features created by its glaciers are part and parcel of the modern southern Alberta scene, preserved from major alteration or destruction in most cases because of the extreme recency of their formation.

It is safe to assume that the glaciers of the southern Rockies behaved in much the same fashion as do those still present in other parts of North America (and in the rest of the world as well, of course). Alpine glaciers are thought to originate as small, isolated patches of snow and ice accumulating in high, protected places, most often on slopes facing north, northeast, or east in the northern hemisphere. The orientation of exposure is important, because northerly, northeasterly, and easterly slopes receive less direct sunshine than those facing in a southerly or southwesterly direction. The result is a tendency for snow in such sites to be preserved, in time to accumulate in sufficient volume and depth for a critical change to ice to take place. Laboratory and field studies have indicated that a snow thickness of 50-75 feet is probably great enough to cause ice to begin to form at its base. Since a glacier, in the simplest sense, is no more than a mass of moving ice, when the buildup of snow has achieved a certain minimal depth on a surface of even very slight inclination, movement can occur and an episode of glaciation properly considered to have begun.

We will never know all the details, but it is not unreasonable to suppose that glaciation in the southern Front Ranges began almost imperceptibly, with masses of snow initially growing to critical size in a few selected high-altitude sites, perhaps in no more than a decade or two but more probably over several hundred years. The precise meteorological conditions favoring glaciation are not completely understood, but a series of slightly cooler, cloudier summers coupled with a number of consecutive winters of somewhat heavier than usual snowfall may have been all that was required. Changes in temperature need not have been more than a few degrees, since once a mass of accumulating snow reaches a certain minimum size, it tends to create its own localized pocket of climate favorable for continued growth.

One can thus envision the gradual development of small, widely scattered glaciers throughout the southern Rockies, each growing in volume and surface area and slowly moving down a pre-existent valley in response to the dictates of gravity. Given sufficient time, coalescence of many small glaciers would lead to formation of the much larger masses of ice that occupied all the major valleys in the Front Ranges.

The number of glacial advances and retreats in the mountains is not known exactly. One of the difficulties inherent in the study of glaciation is that successive advances of ice tend to destroy, or to modify considerably, geomorphologic evidence left by their predecessors. As a result, what we can see in the landscape today is often apt to be only the forms made by the latest glaciers. Nevertheless, there is reasonably good evidence that three or four well-defined episodes of ice advance occurred in the southern Alberta Rockies, the most recent and smallest of which disappeared, high in the mountains, some 6,000-7,000 years ago. The earliest recognizable glaciation appears to have been the most extensive, with ice from the combined Livingstone-Oldman-Crowsnest-Castle drainages moving eastward to a position somewhere between Brocket and Fort Macleod. A massive valley glacier also extended from the mountains into the foothills in the Waterton region, reaching at least as far northeast as the end of Pine Ridge and to perhaps halfway between Mountain View and the park entrance and possibly much farther. Elsewhere along the Rocky Mountain front, valley glaciers seem to have protruded into the foothills only far enough to have formed small piedmont glaciers.

Complicating the matter of unravelling glacial history in the southern Front Ranges is the fact that continental (Laurentide) ice from the north, northeast, and east, arrived at the mountain front *after* the valley glaciers had retreated from positions of maximum advance. Thus, till from the Laurentide ice tends to overlie mountain glacial debris, obscuring what should otherwise be a relatively simple picture. The clearest evidence of the order of advances and retreats by mountain and continental ice is found in cutbank exposures along the larger rivers of the region, where successive layers of Laurentide and alpine till can be seen piled one on top of the other.

In any event, several episodes of Cordilleran glaciation developed in the Rockies, with the earliest and most extensive submerging all of the landscape but the highest ridges and summits beneath hundreds or thousands of feet of ice. Later glaciations, as suggested, were apparently much less impressive, and the last spasm of glacial formation produced only small masses of ice in favored localities along the Continental Divide and in a handful of sheltered positions elsewhere. With the exception of a few tiny accumulations of long-lasting snow and very limited amounts of ice, active glaciation is a thing of the past in the southern Alberta Rockies.

Or is it? At the present time earth scientists are vigorously debating the question of whether or not our planet is really out of the Ice Age or is only in a so-called "interglacial" period. It is known, for example, that glaciers in the European Alps (and in other parts of the earth) have systematically advanced and retreated during the last 1,000 years, although the advances have been much less extensive than those of 15,000-20,000 years ago. Until about the middle or late 1950's, most alpine glaciers in the northern hemisphere had been shrinking at a rapid rate during the 20th century — witness the signs marking successive positions of the toe of the Athabasca glacier in Jasper National Park, which was retreating at an average rate of 60-90 feet per year during the period 1910-1960 *(Figure 16)*. Recently, however, atmospheric temperatures in the northern hemisphere appear to have decreased slightly, and many previously receding glaciers have either slowed their rate of retreat dramatically or, in a few cases, have actually begun a renewed advance. The point is simply that the study of glaciers is far from being a precise science. Man has been observing glacial activity under controlled conditions for less than 150 years, and glacial behavior and the exact causes thereof are still surrounded by many unknowns. On the human time scale the Ice Age obviously seems to have ended, but on the geologic time scale the present may be no more than a momentary pause between successive major glaciations.

The Rocky Mountain region is thus dominated by the direct and indirect effects of glacial activity. Post-glacial time has been so brief (as geologists measure time) that few really significant changes in the glaciated landscape have been produced by other, non-glacial agents of gradation. To the land forms of the present, then, we can now turn our attention.

Rocky Mountain Land Forms
The larger elements of the Rocky Mountain landscape (the Front Ranges and their alternating valleys) are easily identifiable and require little further elaboration. Virtually all of the major and minor valleys were occupied one or more times by ice, and their contemporary appearance is generally that of glaciated canyons little modified by post-glacial

Figure 16. The toe of the Athabasca Glacier as it appeared in July, 1963. Since that time the position of the terminus has migrated several hundred feet upvalley. Tourists continue to ignore the warning signs today!

gradational events. Vegetation has re-established itself throughout much of the mountainous region, but landscape *shapes* still reflect, in the main, the dominant role played by glaciers.

Straight Valleys. One of the more conspicuous geomorphologic results of alpine glaciation is a deepening and straightening of valleys previously affected only by stream action *(Figure 17)*. The more or less linear appearance of Upper Waterton Lake, for example *(Figure 18)*, is a consequence of profound erosion by glaciers which originated mainly in the mountains to the south and moved north into what was to become southwestern Alberta. The pre-glacial

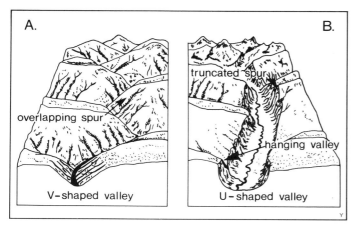

Figure 17. Idealized effects of glaciation in a mountainous region. A. Landscape before glaciation; B. Landscape after glaciation. Not every glaciated canyon in the Alberta Rockies has undergone the indicated "textbook" changes, but many display most of the characteristics here depicted.

valley was deepened and widened by glacial erosion, with spur ridges trimmed off to produce the straight, narrow trough occupied by the lake today. Similarly, canyons tributary to the main Waterton valley tend to be relatively straight or to have only a broadly curving shape in plan *(Figure 19)*. With modifications, most of the glaciated valleys in the southern Front Ranges display this tendency for straightness, affording long, unobstructed vistas into the very heart of the mountains.

U-Shaped Valleys. Because glaciers can effectively erode the sides of valleys and thus plane away overlapping spur ridges *(see Figure 17)*, many glaciated canyons (but certainly not *all*) have a shape in cross-section approximating a broadly flaring "U" *(Figure 20)*. In marked contrast, stream-cut valleys are often noticeably V-shaped. Textbook discussions of alpine glaciation sometimes create the impression that every valley occupied by glacial ice must (and does) have a U-shaped cross section. Even limited observation in the southern Alberta Rockies will reveal that this is not invariably the case, although quite apparently some of the canyons therein do conform nicely to the "textbook" description. However, probably the most significant difference between unglaciated and glaciated valleys

lies in the comparative straightness of the latter, and this landscape characteristic is well developed in our mountains.

Hanging Valleys. Another striking effect of intense alpine glaciation is the creation of so-called "hanging" valleys; these are tributaries of major canyons that join the latter at a higher elevation, literally "hanging" above the floors of the master drainages *(Figure 21)*. Hanging valleys are thought to result when a major canyon undergoes more effective deepening and widening from its larger glacier than can be accomplished by smaller masses of ice in the tributary valleys *(see Figure 17)*. Following disappearance of the ice, mouths of tributaries may be hundreds of feet above the bottom of the trunk canyon. The presence of many waterfalls and steep rapids in glaciated mountains (including the Alberta Rockies) simply reflects the existence of many hanging valleys; the smaller tributary streams must descend precipitously to join the master streams on the floors of the larger canyons. A well-known southern Alberta example is Cameron Falls in Waterton Lakes National Park, which drops to the level of Upper Waterton Lake over a lip of Precambrian rock in the lower, hanging portion of the Cameron Creek drainage *(Figure 22)*.

Cirques. Alpine glaciers originate in areas of snow accumulation and retention. Such sites may be in the heads of pre-glacial valleys or on protected slopes in the upper parts of drainage systems. Many areas in which glaciers have originated have been remodelled by ice action and intense weathering into broad, cliff-walled basins known as *cirques (Figure 23)*. There is no English word for this particular land form; *cirque* is the French term, *corrie, kar,* and *cwm* (pronounced "coomb") are, respectively, the Scottish, German, and Welsh equivalents.

Not every glaciated canyon has a perfect, "textbook" cirque in its upper reaches, but many of the drainage systems in the Alberta Rockies have well-developed cirques in at least some of their uppermost tributaries. Waterton Park is particularly well-endowed with readily accessible cirques (beautifully illustrated on the new official map of the park published in 1973), the floors of a number of which contain small lakes *(Figure 24)*, dammed by masses of glacial debris or low bedrock ridges at the outer edges of the basins. Such lakes are known as *tarns.* Rather frequently, the towering bedrock

Figure 18. Looking south along the valley of Upper Waterton Lake from the Bear's Hump viewpoint. Waterton townsite in foreground.

Figure 19. Valley of Hell Roaring Creek, Waterton Park. The relative straightness and lack of interfingering spur ridges are very apparent.

walls of the cirques will have imposing masses of post-glacial talus rising from the basin floor. Cirques and tarns are thus symptomatic of glacial action and are never found in unglaciated mountains.

Moraines. The rock debris eroded by glacial action, plus material that falls to their surfaces from steep slopes above the glaciers, is incorporated into masses of moving ice, transported down-valley, and ultimately deposited. Deposition of such debris (known as *till*) may occur underneath, at the ends, or along the sides of alpine glaciers, producing a suite of land forms known as *moraines*. Formation of moraines indicates that a critical change has occurred around the margin of a valley glacier — more ice is being lost to melting and other ablation processes than is supplied by replenishment from the accumulation zone high within the mountains. Whatever the cause of this unbalanced condition (and the "experts" are not in agreement on the matter), once ablation begins to exceed

accumulation, glacial retreat must occur, and morainal land forms will often then be formed.

In this connection, it should be emphasized that glacial "retreat" (or "recession") does *not* involve a reversal of direction of flow of the ice. The position of the lower margin of an alpine glacier will retreat or recede when its tongue is losing more volume to ablation than it is gaining by replacement from its source area. Under these circumstances the lower part of the glacier becomes thinner and narrower and the location of the edge of the ice must change, generally shifting toward the area in which the glacier has originated. In the case of an alpine glacier, retreat implies that the position of its toe is moving *up*valley, even though flow of the ice within the body of the glacier may continue to be *down*valley.

All of the Rocky Mountain glaciers in southern Alberta built moraines of one sort or another, although the state of preservation of such features differs notably from canyon to canyon. As mentioned earlier, the arrival of continental ice at the mountain front after retreat of the valley glaciers had occurred has assured that many depositional forms made by

Figure 20. U-shaped valley of a tributary to the Castle River on the east side of Barnaby Ridge.

the valley glaciers in the western Foothills Belt have been buried by Laurentide till. Additionally, the steepness of canyon walls in some drainages has led to post-glacial erosional destruction of ridge-like accumulations of till known as *lateral moraines*. These are deposited along lower valley sides and mark the location of the outer edges or margins of alpine glaciers. Remnants of such moraines are often present, but frequently these are topographically inconspicuous and require considerable searching to find and identify.

Similarly, in many drainage systems, post-glacial stream activity has removed all or most of the material deposited in arcuate ridges of till known as *terminal* and *recessional*

Figure 21. "Textbook" hanging valley (arrow) on the west side of the Castle River south of the ranger station. The floor of the main Castle valley is in the foreground.

moraines. Terminal moraines mark the position of farthest advance of a glacier tongue; they accumulate when the location of the toe or *terminus* remains constant for a time, presumably in response to a condition of balance between gain and loss of volume. Recessional moraines form when the toe of a receding glacier pauses in its retreat, allowing a mass of till to build up around the edge of the ice *(Figure 25). Ground moraine* is a blanket of till deposited *beneath* a glacier rather than along its edges; it usually lacks a recognizable ridge-like or

Figure 22. Cameron Falls, Waterton Lakes National Park, as seen in early Fall.

linear topographic expression, although the surface of a layer of ground moraine may be quite hummocky and irregular.

Morainal remnants can be seen in the lower parts or just outside the mouths of many Rocky Mountain canyons. The Waterton area offers particularly good examples of a number of moraine types. The rolling prairie surface west of the entrance road, best observed from the elevated viewpoint near the buffalo paddock *(Figure 26),* consists of a great complex of glacial depositional forms, including sizable areas of hummocky ground moraine. The long, sloping, tree-covered ridge east of Middle Waterton Lake extending north from the flank of Vimy Peak is a lateral moraine, made probably by the combined depositional action of the main Waterton glacier and a smaller ice mass in Sofa Creek. And clearly observable from the lower Red Rock Canyon road is a well-preserved segment

Figure 23. Cirque on the northeastern flank of Anderson Peak, Waterton Lakes National Park. The mountain is two miles west of Red Rock Canyon.

Figure 24. Crypt Lake, Waterton Park, in the cirque at the head of Hell Roaring Creek. Post-glacial talus, mostly snow-covered in this view, slopes upward from the level of the lake.

Figure 25. Remnant of recessional moraine (arrow) on the floor of Beaver Mines Creek, about three miles upstream from Beaver Mines townsite. The creek has breached the moraine in post-glacial time.

Figure 26. Hummocky ground moraine in Waterton Park as seen from near the Buffalo Paddock. The view looks southwest toward Mt. Crandell.

of ridge-like moraine at the northern end of the golf course that was deposited along the common margin of the Waterton and Blakiston glaciers where they merged *(Figure 27)*. Post-glacial erosion by Blakiston Brook has cut through this moraine, nicely exposing its internal structure. Morainal land forms, then, are widespread along the mountain front and in a number of lower canyons. Their presence represents unmistakeable evidence of the depositional action of valley glaciers. The excellent state of preservation of many morainal features is still another geomorphologic reminder of the recency of glaciation in the Front Ranges.

Figure 27. Ridge-like morainal remnant at the north end of the golf course, Waterton Lakes National Park. Blakiston Brook in foreground, northern flank of Mt. Crandall in background.

Stream Terraces. Visible in parts of the courses of all the largest drainage systems in the southern Rockies are segments of well-preserved stream terraces. These are smooth, gently sloping surfaces flanking the rivers and conspicuous by virtue of their topographic contrast with the adjacent terrain. Ten such terrace sets have been identified in the Oldman River valley east of the Livingstone Range *(Figure 28)*, and nine or ten are present in the lower Crowsnest valley *(Figure 29)*. The Castle and Carbondale rivers also have several suites of terraces

Figure 28. Stream terraces (the smooth, light-colored surfaces in the middle ground) in the valley of the Oldman River a mile or so east of the Gap.

in their middle and lower reaches. In most places the material underlying the terraces is relatively coarse sand and gravel, much of which is rounded rather than angular, and is generally arranged in readily recognizable beds or layers. The physical characteristics and crude stratification of the terrace materials are a clear indication of the fact that the sands and gravels were transported and deposited primarily by running water.

What are we to make of these interesting land forms? They are found in valleys that obviously were glaciated, but the terraces are not the product of direct glacial action. In the main, they are made of *glacial outwash,* fragmental rock material moved a certain distance by ice and subsequently transported and deposited beyond the ice margin by meltwater streams. The terraces were built at the end of the most recent episode of glaciation and are believed to have originated as follows:

Figure 29. Stream terraces in the Crowsnest River valley just north of Lundbreck.

1. We have noted that glaciers in the mountains had already retreated from positions of maximum advance by the time continental ice reached southwestern Alberta. As recession of the mountain glaciers occurred, large volumes of rock debris were transported beyond the ice limits by meltwater streams, some of which was deposited in lower stream courses.

2. As Laurentide ice approached and in some places reached the mountain front, lakes fed by meltwater streams issuing from the waning alpine glaciers were formed in the Foothills Belt, dammed between the edge of the advancing continental glacier and higher ground to the west.

3. As lake levels rose, overall gradients of the meltwater streams must have been lessened, since the levels of the lakes into which they were draining set effective limits to the steepness of gradient attainable by any given stream *(Figure 30)*. Decreased stream gradients led to decreased velocities of flow, with an attendant loss of transporting power. The result was deposition of much of the coarse outwash material in middle and lower stream courses.

4. In time, wasting of the edge of the continental ice occurred; accordingly, its damming effect was lessened and lake levels began to fall. As they did, stream gradients were steepened and velocities increased, and the resultant increase in erosive ability enabled the streams to cut into the masses of outwash. Each terrace level, or tread, represents the former floor of a downcutting stream, and since all of the larger rivers have several sets of terraces, it is probable that downcutting was intermittent.

5. With ultimate disappearance of the continental ice, the stream systems of the present began to organize themselves in the western plains. Downcutting by the rivers in the mountains continued, although probably at a decreasing rate. The terraces remain as evidence of a most intriguing sequence of late-glacial events.

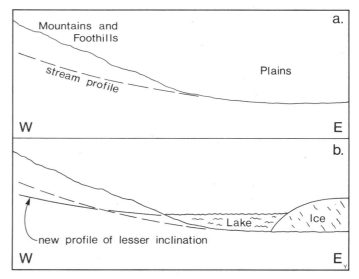

Figure 30. Diagrammatic representation showing effect on stream gradients of formation of lakes in the lower foothills zone. A. Conditions before arrival of Laurentide glacier; B. Stream continues to cut down in mountains, but rising lake level gives to its overall profile a gentler gradient, leading to deposition of outwash.

What is important to keep in mind about this simplified account is that the presence of such terraces in a valley indicates beyond dispute that two different but related geomorphologic episodes must have taken place: (1) The stream in the valley has experienced a period of deposition (for whatever reason); and (2) the same stream has subsequently acquired sufficient erosive power to cut away much of the previously deposited material (again, for whatever reason). In the present instance, glaciation, directly and indirectly, provided the reasons. *Figure 31* illustrates in more or less idealized fashion the sequence of necessary geomorphologic steps leading to the terraced landscapes of the present.

Special Features. Undoubtedly a rather sizable volume could be compiled describing what one observer or another might consider "special" about specific aspects of the Rocky Mountain landscape. Three particularly interesting geomorphologic features are noted here, with no claim that they are necessarily the most unusual or dramatically scenic

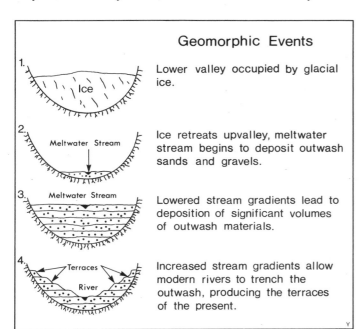

Geomorphic Events

1. Lower valley occupied by glacial ice.

2. Ice retreats upvalley, meltwater stream begins to deposit outwash sands and gravels.

3. Lowered stream gradients lead to deposition of significant volumes of outwash materials.

4. Increased stream gradients allow modern rivers to trench the outwash, producing the terraces of the present.

Figure 31. Hypothetical development of terraces: (1) Alpine glacier present in valley; (2) glacier recedes, deposition of outwash begins; (3) formation of lake at lower end of river leads to decrease in gradient and increase in amount of deposition; (4) drainage of lake with deglaciation on the plains produces steeper stream gradient.

parts of the mountains; they simply happen to appear to the author as being worthy of more than passing attention. These are (1) the *Frank Slide,* which nearly everyone, I suspect, would agree is something "special", (2) the *Gap* of the *Oldman River* through the Livingstone Range, and (3) an excellent example of so-called *patterned ground* on top of Plateau Mountain in the Front Ranges.

The Frank Slide

Most southern Albertans are familiar with the Frank Slide and know at least the general outline of its history. Briefly, at about 4:10 a.m. on April 29, 1903, part of the eastern side of the summit of Turtle Mountain broke free and plummetted into the Crowsnest valley, partially obliterating the south side of the young town of Frank, burying the railroad and highway to depths of 100 feet or more, and rushing across the valley floor to climb a few hundred feet up the opposite slope. An estimated 90 million tons of rock were involved in the slide, making it one of the largest known to have occurred on earth in the past few thousand years. Although this spectacular event happened more than 70 years ago, the appearance of the slide scar on Turtle Mountain and the great mass of shattered debris on the valley floor is remarkably fresh *(Figure 32).* Boulders as large as 40-50 feet are found in the slide, but the average size of fragmental debris is considerably smaller *(Figure 33).*

Two aspects of the slide have long intrigued both the general public and earth scientists with a special interest in mass-movement phenomena of this type, its *cause* and the *mechanism of movement* by which the great sheet of broken rock was spread so widely across the valley floor. So far as the *cause* is concerned, geologic opinion is all but unanimous in declaring that the exceptionally steep slopes on the eastern side of Turtle Mountain and the fundamental structural characteristics of the mountain were the two *primary* factors leading to the slide. The top of Turtle Mountain consists of a tightly folded anticline, the eastern limb of which dips sharply toward the Crowsnest valley *(Figure 34).* The mass of rock making up the slide initially moved downward along *bedding planes* in the limestone strata that constitute much of the bulk of the mountain. Bedding planes are simply surfaces of separation between adjacent layers of rock and are potential zones of weakness in any accumulation of sediments.

Most of Turtle Mountain (approximately the upper two-thirds) is part of a massive block of limestone (the

Figure 32. Turtle Mountain and the Frank Slide as seen from north of Bellevue.

Blairmore Range) that has moved eastward along a thrust fault to override younger rocks, mainly sandstones and shales with interbedded coal seams. Mining of coal in the steeply dipping beds at the base of the mountain *(see Figure 34)* has long been believed by many people to have been the *direct* cause of the slide. However, evidence collected shortly after the event does not support this interpretation. A number of men were at work inside the mine on the morning of April 29, 1903, and their collective testimony indicated that although a certain amount of coal was dislodged at the time of the slide, no really significant movement of the rock walls occurred in the tunnel in which they were trapped. Thus, a large slippage or shifting of bedrock at the base of the mountain appears not to have taken place, and the immediate cause of the slide could not have been a collapse of rock within the mine. On the other hand, it is only reasonable to assume (as most geologists have done) that removal of large volumes of coal and rock in the course of mining certainly contributed to a general weakening of the eastern flank of Turtle Mountain, adding to the dangers of an already unstable natural situation.

The "triggering" event that set the slide in motion can probably never be pinpointed exactly. Although the evidence is not as clear as it might be, substantial fissures or fractures apparently were present in exposed bedrock at the top of

Figure 33. Scar of the Frank Slide on Turtle Mountain and part of the great sheet of debris on the valley floor. Note the light color of small, fresh slides below the high peak at the left; these slides are also visible in Figure 32.

the slide in motion. This, indeed, was the conclusion reached by two members of the Geological Survey of Canada who examined the slide shortly after its occurrence and submitted a comprehensive report on June 12, 1903. On the other hand, the "trigger" that initiated movement may have had no relationship whatsoever to the weather. A minor local earthquake, for example, too small to have been detected by the seismic instruments then in use, could also have provided the "trigger".

In any event, once movement had begun, the great mass of rock fell down the side of Turtle Mountain and spread rapidly across the valley, the whole affair reportedly requiring no more than 100 seconds. What strikes an observant visitor is the enormous extent of the sheet of debris on the valley floor. What is equally impressive is the general lack of great piles of fragmented rock at the immediate base of the mountain; this latter condition can readily be seen by traversing the gravel road through the slide between the railway and the Crowsnest River. Absence of large volumes of debris close to the base of the mountain and the great horizontal extent of the slide have puzzled investigating geologists for decades. If the piece of Turtle Mountain that broke loose from the summit had simply slipped directly down the steep eastern slope, staying more or

Turtle Mountain before the slide occurred. The month of March, 1903, was very snowy in the southern Front Ranges, judging from meteorological records kept at Pincher Creek, and local weather conditions immediately before the disaster were possibly of critical importance. It was reported to have been unseasonably warm for several days prior to April 29, but temperatures early that morning dropped to well below freezing, perhaps as low as zero. It can be speculated (though not *proven*) that large volumes of meltwater from a heavy snow cover must have poured into the mountain-top fissures during the mild days preceding the slide, and that freezing of this water on the night of April 28-29 produced sufficient pressures deep within the fissures to have wedged or pried loose a large mass of rock. Given the basic natural instability of the upper part of the mountain, coupled with further weakening as a result of mining at its eastern base, the effects of freezing in deep fissures may have been just enough to set

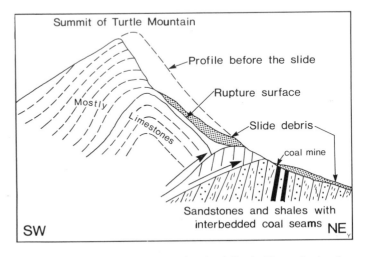

Figure 34. NE-SW cross-sectional sketch of Turtle Mountain showing fundamental structural features. The Frank Slide initially moved down bedding plains in the steeply dipping limestone on the eastern limb of the Turtle Mountain anticline.

less in contact with the ground while moving, it would be logical to expect that most of the debris should have piled up at the foot of the slope, even allowing that momentum would have carried some of it out onto the main valley floor. Yet this is quite evidently *not* what happened, and there remains the problem of accounting for the disposition of the great sheet of broken rock.

Without going into the mathematics of the situation, suffice it to note that many geologists are now convinced the behavior of the Frank Slide, and others of comparable size and character, can be explained satisfactorily as being the result of *air-layer lubrication.* The term means just what the words imply: The mass of fragmental debris rode out over the valley on a layer of trapped, compressed air. Only in this way, it has been postulated, is it possible to account for the great horizontal extent of the slide, parts of the perimeter of which are nearly two airline miles from the summit of Turtle Mountain. As envisioned by proponents of the air-layer lubrication concept, the Frank Slide started from the top of the mountain as a relatively coherent block of rock, the block fell about 2,500 vertical feet (probably breaking up in the process), the shattered mass of limestone was deflected into the air by a projecting shelf of rock near the base of the slope, and most of the deflected mass then overrode and trapped a layer of air on which it literally slid to its present location. The cushion of compressed air would have been essentially frictionless, allowing easy and rapid passage of a sheet of fragmented but interlocking debris, and when sufficient air had leaked through and from around the edges of the mass, movement would have abruptly stopped.

Is there any available evidence that might support this patently outrageous idea? Since the slide occurred before daylight, there were no actual *eye*witnesses to the main event. However, interviews were held with a number of people who were positioned close to the edge of the slide and survived, and several of these mentioned feeling or seeing the effects of great blasts of air apparently issuing from around its fringes; the noise was described as "resembling that of steam escaping under high pressure". That large volumes of compressed air escaped with high velocity from the edges of the slide seems beyond dispute. Furthermore, the margins of the slide are steep and sharp, suggesting (but not *proving*) that movement must have stopped comparatively suddenly, the fragmented mass of rock simply being let down in place as its forward motion ceased. The air-layer lubrication theory, however unlikely it may seem at first blush, at least does offer a reasonable and physically feasible mechanism of movement to account for the great distance covered by the slide on the valley floor; it also explains the general lack of debris at the foot of Turtle Mountain, as well as the apparent rapidity of the whole event. But it admittedly remains a bitter mental pill for many people to swallow!

The Frank Slide is a landscape feature of unique geologic and historic interest, not only to local and regional residents, but to earth scientists from all over the world. Three generations of geology and geomorphology students have read about and studied pictures of the slide, and many of them have gone out of their way to come to southern Alberta specifically to visit the site. It is to be fervently hoped that the millions of tons of limestone in the slide will not be sacrificed to commercial interests, ending up ignominiously as concrete symbols (both literally and figuratively) of man's seemingly insatiable greed.

Figure 35. The Gap of the Oldman River through the southern Livingstone Range as seen from high on the south side of the canyon. View is toward the northeast.

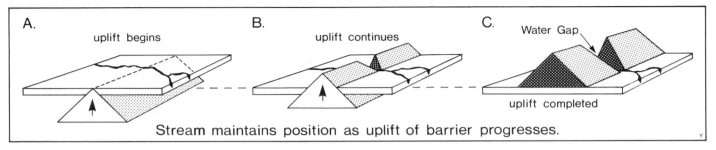

Figure 36. Production of a water gap by *antecedence*. While the barrier is slowly uplifted tectonically, the stream remains at the same elevation, thus cutting its way through the rising barrier to erode the water gap.

The Gap

Slashing across the southern Livingstone Range in an S-shaped course, the Oldman River flows through a spectacular canyon known as the Gap *(Figure 35)*. The Livingstone Range at this particular place consists mainly of westerly dipping beds of limestone, and because of a relatively sparse vegetation cover through the canyon, the structure is remarkably clear. What is not so clear is why the Gap is where it is and how it got that way.

In order to explain the existence and location of canyons such as the Gap (known technically as *water gaps*), geologists and geomorphologists have devised two possible models of origin and have attached the terms *antecedence* and *superposition* (also *superimposition*) to them. The terms refer to two different supposed sequences of geomorphic events, as follows:

Antecedence implies that a stream was present in a particular location before (*antecedent* to) differential tectonic uplift of the barrier across which it now cuts. In this model it is assumed that uplift has been so slow that the stream was not deflected but was able to maintain its initial course even as the barrier was raised, in effect cutting its way through the rising ridge or mountain range during the episode of uplift *(Figure 36.)*

Superposition is believed to occur when a stream flowing on a once higher surface cuts downward as the general regional elevation decreases with time, in this way being let down on (*superimposed* upon) a more-resistant buried structural feature

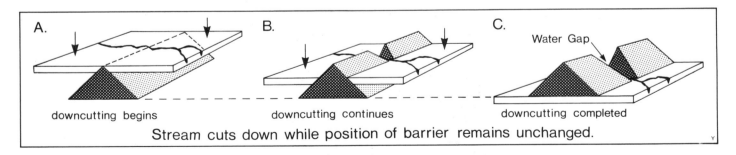

Figure 37. Creation of a water gap by *superposition.* The elevation of the barrier remains the same, but the stream cuts down through it as the regional elevation is lowered. The final land form — the water gap — is essentially the same in both cases.

that will become exposed as general regional lowering continues *(Figure 37).* In both cases the final result is approximately the same — a river flowing through a somewhat anomolous gash across a more or less continuous ridge or mountain barrier.

Two obvious questions about the Gap of the Oldman River present themselves: Is it the result of antecedence or superposition, and why does it happen to be exactly where it is (that is, why not six miles north or three miles south?)? Answers to both are not so easy to come by. If the Livingstone Range were offset by faulting at the Gap site (as has happened in other parts of the Canadian Rockies), a clue to at least its location would be available. It could then be argued that the collective runoff from the Livingstone and upper Oldman drainages took advantage of the "break" in the otherwise continuous wall of the Livingstone Range and exploited the weaker, fragmented rock along the line of the fault. But there is no evidence of such a fault-produced break at the Gap; rocks north and south of the canyon show little or no indication of having been offset horizontally by faulting. Evidently an explanation will have to be based upon some other causal factor.

A feasible history of structural and geomorphologic events leading to the present condition of the Gap can be sketched. As indicated earlier in this chapter, orogenic activity in the Rocky Mountain region seems to have been intermittent during the last 100 million years; periods of orogeny appear to have been interspersed with times of comparative tectonic quiescence, during which gradational processes must have operated to wear down the high-standing, tectonically produced forms. The most recent major tectonic event was regional uplift of the whole Rocky Mountain region a few million years before the onset of Pleistocene glaciation. It is not unreasonable to suppose that overall relief in the area of the present-day mountains was considerably subdued prior to broad-scale uplift; the regional surface may well have been comparatively smooth and the great thrust-slabs of older limestones partially or completely buried by rocks of different type and younger age. A hypothetical cross-section in the vicinity of the modern Livingstone Range is shown in *Figure 38.* At that time, it can be speculated, the ancestral Oldman-Livingstone drainage system was flowing on a surface that bevelled all of the embryonic Front Ranges (including the Livingstone Range), its course determined by the topographic features then in existence.

Regional uplift and possibly a certain amount of tilting toward the east caused all of the streams to become faster and thus more effective as erosional agents; in geological parlance, the rivers were *rejuvenated.* Accordingly, the trunk streams and their tributaries began to cut down, and their gradational work was probably more successful in the younger, weaker rocks than in the limestones of the Front Ranges to be.

This sequential combination of geological and geomorphological circumstances led, in time, to the landscapes of the present. More effective erosion in the weaker rocks of the mountainous area produced excavation of valleys; faulting may also have played a role in formation of some of the valleys. As erosion progressed, certain streams, including the Oldman-Livingstone, were let down on, or *superposed* upon, the emerging ranges of the modern Rockies, and excavation of the valley of the Gap began.

The model of development proposed here thus attributes the origin of the Gap to superposition; the Oldman River is a *superposed stream* at this site. However, the model does not explain why the Gap is precisely where we find it today. About the most that can be said regarding its specific location is that the ancestral Oldman River must have been in approximately its present geographical position when downcutting induced by epeirogenic uplift began. Once the downcutting river became even slightly incised in the Livingstone Range, a shift in its course through the emerging mountain wall would have been most unlikely. With the passage of time and continuing erosion by the river, the

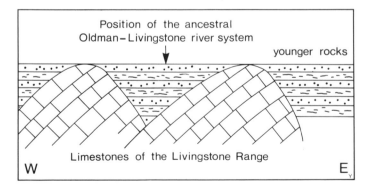

Figure 38. Hypothetical cross-sectional sketch showing conditions in the vicinity of the modern Livingstone Range prior to uplift and regional tilting of southern Rockies. As the ancestral river cut down during general regional lowering, it became *superposed* on the Livingstone Range, thus initiating formation of the Gap.

canyon was deepened and widened, and the modern Gap developed. Glacial ice from the mountains to the west moved through the Gap at least three times, undoubtedly modifying the river-cut canyon to a certain extent. With the end of glaciation in the mountains, the present-day streams became established, and the combined flow of the upper Oldman-Livingstone rivers was funneled through the Gap.

This reconstruction of possible events leading to formation of the Gap is admittedly speculative in many details. But at least it does no great violence to the geologic and geomorphologic facts of the case and does seem to offer a reasonable explanation for the observable characteristics of this most interesting landscape feature.

Patterned Ground
on Plateau Mountain

Plateau Mountain is in the easternmost Front Ranges west of Nanton. Its summit is a broad, smooth, treeless surface at an elevation of 8,000-8,200 feet; the geologic structure underlying the "plateau" is an elongated anticlinal dome of limestone capped by a very hard, resistant quartz sandstone *(Figure 39)*. The top of Plateau Mountain evidently was not glaciated during Pleistocene time, so it must have stood above the surrounding ice surface as a *nunatak*; the word is Eskimo and means "lonely peak". Access to the top of the mountain is relatively easy by way of a road leading to several wells of the Savanna Creek gas field on the summit.

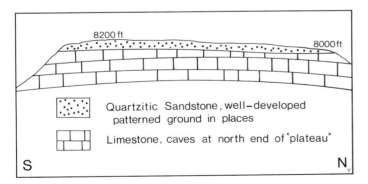

8200 ft   8000 ft

:::::: Quartzitic Sandstone, well-developed patterned ground in places

▭▭▭ Limestone, caves at north end of 'plateau'

S   N

Figure 39. Generalized cross-sectional sketch showing structural conditions and rock types at the summit of Plateau Mountain.

Figure 40. Patterned ground at the south end of Plateau Mountain. The segregation of larger stones into a circular or polygonal pattern is apparent. View is toward the southeast.

Prominently developed on parts of Plateau Mountain is an extensive area of *patterned ground (Figure 40),* a surface configuration made up of accumulations of larger pieces of rock in polygonal or circular patterns, with finer materials in the centres. Most earth scientists who have investigated this feature (it is widespread in arctic and sub-arctic Canada) believe it to be fundamentally a product of cold, harsh climatic conditions. Much of the patterned ground now known is found in high-latitude or high-altitude areas, or in regions believed to have had a more severe climate at some time in the past. So-called "active" patterned ground is currently undergoing development and alteration, while inactive or "fossil" patterned ground seems to be experiencing little or no change under contemporary conditions. The patterned ground on Plateau Mountain probably belongs in the latter category.

There is no general agreement on details of the origin of most patterned ground. Two aspects of this landscape feature require explanation: (1) the pattern itself, which can be almost geometrically perfect or, on occasion, highly irregular; and (2) the sorting or segregation of the larger blocks of rock from the finer particles in the centres of polygons or circles.

Probably a majority of geologists and geomorphologists who have studied patterned ground in high northern latitudes would accept the proposition that cracking of the ground as a result of thermal contraction (due to cooling) is responsible for the initiation of surface fissures that make up the basic geometrical network of much patterned ground. Laboratory and field experiments have clearly demonstrated that deep cooling of surficial earth materials will produce contraction and a breaking apart of soil, often in a highly symmetrical,

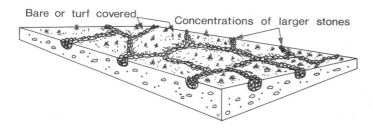

Bare or turf covered. Concentrations of larger stones

Figure 41. Typical arrangement of stone distribution in an area of well-developed patterned ground. The patterned ground on Plateau Mountain seems to be of this type.

patterned fashion. Shrinkage due to a drying-out of finer-grained materials will also produce a regular pattern of fissures; this process is known as *desiccation cracking* and can be observed on a small scale almost every time a mud puddle dries up, leaving behind a thin film of cracked and patterned clay. Seasonal low temperatures and intermittent drying out of the soil are thus probably primary factors in the development of the *pattern* in much patterned ground.

On the other hand, the processes of sorting or segregation of the larger and smaller materials are much less well understood, although it is assumed by many that seasonal formation of ice in the soil is a significant factor in many cases. Excavations in areas of patterned ground have revealed that the larger pieces of rock often occupy trench-like, linear depressions among the "islands" of finer surficial debris *(Figure 41)*. The "trenches" are thought to develop along

surface cracks produced by thermal contraction, possibly as a result of erosional removal of clays, silts, and fine sands during periods of surface runoff. The problem, then, is how to account for concentration of blocks of rock in the trenches. It is known that in a mass of earth materials subjected to alternate freezing and thawing, there is a pronounced tendency for the coarser rocks to work their way upward toward and eventually to the surface; the process is known as *frost sorting* and is graphically demonstrated in cultivated fields that seem to "grow" a crop of stones in the spring. Once at the surface, it is possible that differential heaving by ice formation in the soil could push, wedge, or slide the larger blocks toward and ultimately into the trench-like depressions, thus bringing about the concentration of coarser debris that is such a notable characteristic of much patterned ground. However, details of many of the supposed processes are poorly understood, at best, and a complete explanation of the origin of most patterned ground is lacking today.

The patterned ground on Plateau Mountain very likely is a relic of the Ice Age, formed when the top of the mountain was an "island", a lonely peak in a sea of glacial ice. It is a reasonable speculation that the Pleistocene climate of the Plateau Mountain nunatak was considerably colder (and possibly wetter) than that of the present. Thermal contraction of surficial materials, coupled with soil heaving related to seasonal freeze and thaw, in time produced the patterning and sorting of larger rocks that constitute the basic morphologic characteristics of the feature. With disappearance of the ice and, presumably, an amelioration of climate, active development of the patterning and sorting has ceased, leaving the conspicuous features of the present as an excellent example of "fossil" patterned ground.

The Rockies – Summary

From the top of Crowsnest Mountain to the shoreline of Waterton Lake, the Rocky Mountain landscape is dramatic *(Figure 42)*. Slopes are steep, topographic relief is great, and vast areas of bare bedrock are strikingly on display. Tectonic activity on a massive scale was responsible, directly or indirectly, for the building of the larger physiographic units of the region, the generally linear Front Ranges. Beginning as long as 100 million years ago, orogenic activity has been intermittent in the Rockies, reaching culminating episodes at perhaps 60 million years and again at about 4-6 million years. A few million years before the onset of extensive glaciation, broad, regional uplift led to elevation of the southern Rockies by several thousands of feet. However, even as folding, faulting, and uplift occurred, running water and gravity, the two most pervasive of the gradational agents, must have been at work, functioning to counteract the effects of the tectonic processes. As the time of glaciation approached, the *general*

appearance of the Rocky Mountain region was probably not greatly unlike that of the present.

With the advent of the Ice Age, powerfully erosive valley glaciers assumed a prominent role in landscape history, inexorably moving downslope to widen, straighten, and deepen most pre-glacial valleys. As the mountain glaciers retreated and finally disappeared only a few thousand years ago, the landscapes of the present emerged, and running water and gravity were re-established as the dominant agents of gradation. Details of the glaciated landscape have been altered in places by the modern streams, but the overall impression in much of the area is still that of a mountainous region evacuated by the ice as recently as a geological "yesterday".

Figure 42. Upper Crowsnest valley and the High Rock Range as seen from west of Coleman.

CHAPTER 4
THE FOOTHILLS BELT

In terms of areal extent and geologic grandeur, the foothills of southwestern Alberta undeniably lack the bold, stark scenery of the mountains or the seemingly limitless expanse of the plains. Confined to a long, narrow strip immediately east of the Rocky Mountain front, this geomorphologic region may appear at first glance to be but a pale copy of the Front Ranges, stunted in its growth and squeezed into a slim zone of little interest save to the petroleum geologist, coal miner, logger, or rancher. But first appearances — or glances — are often deceiving, and the foothills deserve far more than casual mention.

An outstanding geomorphologic feature of much of the Foothills Belt is the tendency for its landscape to be dominated by long, low, roughly parallel ridges with a general northwest-southeast orientation. In the main, the surface topography here is a pretty direct reflection of the sub-surface geologic structure. The western boundary of the foothills zone is represented by the pronounced topographic break at the eastern edge of the Rocky Mountain Front Ranges. In contrast, the eastern margin is usually much less conspicuous and may be recognizable by little more than a modest change from an essentially horizontal surface to one of only very gently rolling aspect.

To the geologist, the foothills region is characterized by very distinctive subsurface structure — the term "disturbed belt" has been applied to this particular geologic province in reference to the intricate dislocations sustained by many of the rocks therein. Thus, even though the Porcupine Hills would seem topographically to be part and parcel of the foothills, the geological purist would classify them as belonging to the plains because they lack the folding and thrust-faulting so well-developed in the foothills proper. For our purposes, the Porcupine Hills will be discussed in this chapter since the emphasis here is on surface form, or geomorphology, and the Porcupines logically and geographically seem to be a part of the general foothills region. The structural geologist may object, but the differences between "true" foothills and the Porcupine Hills will be made clear.

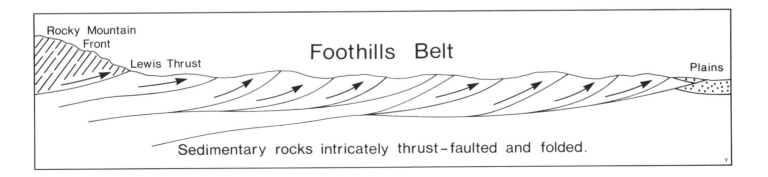

Figure 43. Generalized cross-sectional sketch showing subsurface structural conditions in the southern Foothills Belt. Many of the thrust faults have been omitted for purposes of clarity, but the basic structural pattern is shown correctly.

Foothills Structure

Stretching northwesterly from the international boundary to beyond Jasper National Park, the Alberta Foothills Belt closely parallels the eastern edge of the Rocky Mountains. Its average width throughout this considerable latitudinal extent is perhaps 15-25 miles. Almost anywhere within this zone a northeast-southwest structural cross-section would resemble in its broader features that depicted in *Figure 43,* which shows subsurface conditions in the southern foothills between Waterton Lakes National Park and Pincher Creek. Details may

Figure 44. Tightly folded bedrock along the channel of the Oldman River about 6 miles east of the Gap. The structure revealed here is an anticline, with more steeply dipping beds on the left and layers with gentler inclination on the right. Note the smooth stream terraces in the background.

vary from place to place, but the pattern of overlapping thrust faults is repeated, giving rise to slices of rock of different age and type stacked one on top of the other. Geologically, the transition from faulted and folded beds to more or less horizontal strata marks the outer, or eastern, limit of the Foothills Belt. Along most of the belt this change occurs at the surface, but in places the "disturbed" condition continues at depth east of the horizontal rocks at the surface. As noted above, the eastern margin of the Foothills Belt is topographically much less pronounced than the striking

western boundary, but there generally is a recognizable change across a zone of transition from a horizontal or only slightly undulating surface to a landscape distinctively more "hilly". In driving from Cardston to Waterton Park, for example, this change occurs about two miles west of Cardston where the highway crosses the first low northwest-southeast ridge of the foothills proper.

Considerable information about foothills structure has been gained over the past 40-50 years, largely as a result of exploration activities by the oil industry. Systematic study of subsurface conditions in the Waterton, Pincher Creek, Savanna Creek, and Turner Valley fields (all but the latter producing only natural gas) has led to the discovery of exceptionally complex structural features, the presence of which could simply not be determined (or even suspected) from surface investigations alone. What the subsurface information reveals is the presence of relatively thin slices of rocks of different age and type pushed or thrust eastward along a multitude of low-angle fault surfaces, resulting in a shortening and thickening (or *telescoping*) of a great mass of upper Paleozoic and Mesozoic formations throughout the Foothills Belt. Rather frequently, older rocks are found thrust above younger formations. In places, the complexities of subsurface conditions are suggested by readily observable surface features *(Figure 44),* but in most of the zone the surface indications are but a figurative "tip of the iceberg". Of primary interest to the oil industry have been the location and structural characteristics of older limestone formations, since in virtually all cases these are the reservoir rocks for accumulations of gaseous and liquid hydrocarbons.

As previously noted, the Foothills Belt is believed by most geologists to represent the easternmost part of a much more extensive area affected by mountain-building forces in western Canada. The record of the rocks suggests that orogenic activity started in the western part of the Rocky Mountain region and moved eastward with the passage of time, thus making the foothills structures the youngest within the larger area. Beginning perhaps in early Mesozoic time, thrust faulting and folding migrated toward the east, building first the great linear Front Ranges and ultimately producing the foothills. Details of the precise causes of the migrating episodes of tectonism remain obscure, but the effects are readily apparent, both in the main Rocky Mountains and the nearby foothills.

It is highly probable that a complete explanation of the origin of the Foothills Belt (and the Rockies to the west) will involve consideration of the so-called "new geology", a catch-all term for the revolution in the earth sciences of the last couple of decades. In the model of the earth presently emerging, the old idea of continental drift has been modified and combined with more recent discoveries about the floors of the oceans. Within the past ten years, a scheme of development of the earth's larger surface structural features based upon the concept of moving surficial slabs of rock (or *plates*) has been proposed. In the new geology, tectonic activity (including earthquakes and vulcanism) is assumed to be confined mainly to linear zones of contact and interaction between adjacent plates, hence the term *plate tectonics*.

Formation of the whole mountainous region of western Canada (including its easternmost extension, the Alberta foothills) is explained as being a consequence of the overriding of a great surface slab (the Pacific plate) by the relatively westerly moving North American plate. Effects of this supposed tectonic event have been most intense in the mountains of interior British Columbia; the Alberta foothills structures are thus only the easternmost manifestation of a related series of orogenic episodes of much greater areal extent and complexity.

Details of the proposed sequence of interrelated processes are incompletely understood and debatable, but an increasing number of earth scientists find in the new geology a grand, unifying theme in the physical history of the earth. Included in the list of suggested references at the end of this volume are several recent books containing a synthesis of the collection of ideas that encompass the basic concepts of the new geology; these are highly recommended to anyone with an interest in the topic.

Foothills Landscapes

As is true of landscapes in any part of the earth's surface, those of the Alberta Foothills Belt are a product of the interactions between two opposed sets of forces, the internal or tectonic processes and the external or gradational processes. As described in Chapter 1, the former operate to elevate parts of the earth's crust, to create relief, while the latter function to wear down the tectonically produced forms. The amount of relief and degree of ruggedness of a landscape are thus indirect measures of the intensity of operation of the opposing sets of forces — generally speaking, the higher and steeper the terrain, the more effective have been the tectonic forces. At the same time, even as relief increases, the agents of gradation, particularly running water and gravity, tend to operate more efficiently, so that any high-standing piece of the crust is

Figure 45. Steeply dipping sandstone beds of the Foothills Belt just west of Lundbreck. The crest of the Livingstone Range is visible along the left side of the skyline.

doomed, ultimately, to gradational destruction. The "everlasting hills" are far from that; the higher they are, the more rapidly will they be worn away!

Quite apparently, relief and ruggedness in the Foothills Belt are subdued and muted in contrast to the Rockies. Most of the region is in slopes, but these tend to be gentle and short in comparison with those of the mountains. The inference is clear: Tectonic processes, although obviously active at some time in the past, have produced a much less spectacular structural landscape here, and the gradational forces, with considerably less relief to work with, have operated at a much lower intensity than in the Front Ranges. The net result is a hilly, rolling landscape in most of the Foothills Belt in which structural control of individual elements is prominent.

As a general rule, ridges in the foothills are underlain by sandstone bedrock. The reason is simply that sandstones tend to be more resistant to weathering and erosion under foothills climatic conditions than are shales and other fine-grained rocks. Since most of the rock formations in the Foothills Belt consist of alternating layers of sandstone and shale, it is understandable that, given sufficient time, differential

Figure 46. Anticlinal fold in bedrock underlying a ridge in the Foothills Belt. The location is between Burmis and Tod Creek.

weathering and erosion have acted to create a landscape in which the harder rocks tend to form the topographically higher elements. A view looking north over the Crowsnest River from just west of Lundbreck *(Figure 45)* illustrates the point nicely. Here, bedrock is steeply tilted toward the east (this is clearly visible in the section exposed at the river's edge), and the ridge with scattered trees on the horizon consists of a northward continuation of the layered rocks next to the river. Most of these are sandstones, and their superior resistance to gradational lowering accounts for the topographic prominence of the ridge. The lower ground both east and west of the ridge is on shales and other more-easily eroded rocks.

In some parts of the foothills zone, ridges are held up by upfolded (or anticlinal) geologic structures *(Figure 46)*, in which case there is a direct relationship between structure and topography. As a general rule, however, such a one-to-one relationship does not prevail, since gradational processes have had enough time to exploit the weaknesses of the less-resistant rocks and have more successfully worn down the shales to form valleys. The usual correlation between foothills topography and geology, then, is for ridges to be underlain by tougher sandstones and lower terrain to be cut in shales, whatever the fundamental structure may be.

In other parts of the foothills region, the land forms offer absolutely no clue to underlying structure. This may especially be the case in the immediate vicinity of the larger rivers, where gradational action by the streams has eroded simple or intricate bedrock structures to form an almost horizontal surface *(Figure 47;* see also *Figure 44).* In these instances, the smooth bedrock surface has often been covered by stream or glacial deposits, and only examination of exposures in the walls of the valleys allows a true appreciation of the structural situation to be gained.

Most of the Foothills Belt was overrun one or more times by glacial ice. However, the effects of glaciation in this region appear to have been far less pronounced (in terms of *major* landscape changes) than they were in the Rockies or on the plains. Ice from the north and east (the Laurentide glacier) reached the edge of the mountains at least once, indicating that virtually all of the foothills region must have been influenced by continental glaciers. Additionally, valley glaciers from the Front Ranges extended well into the foothills in several places. Yet in much of the area, land forms are not particularly suggestive of very effective glacial action. Rather frequently, the only readily recognizable surficial evidence of glaciation will be the presence of scattered *erratics,* pieces of rock of a type different from the underlying bedrock (hence

Figure 47. Dipping beds of sandstone and shale along the Castle River south of Cowley. The tilted strata have been planed off by river action and covered with horizontal layers of stream gravels and sands.

Figure 48-A. Big Rock of the Foothills Erratics Train west of Okotoks. The rock has been broken into several pieces by weathering after deposition in its present position.

Figure 48-B. Closer view of the Big Rock. The above-ground dimensions of this erratic are 135 x 60 x 30 feet and it has an estimated weight of 18,000 tons, making it one of the largest, if not *the* largest, of the glacial erratics in North America.

considered to be *erratic* in their distribution) that were transported by glaciers to their present positions. Most erratics in the Foothills Belt are blocks of igneous or metamorphic rock from the Canadian Shield; their presence in southwestern Alberta, hundreds of miles from the place of origin, represents unequivocal evidence of large-scale continental glaciation here.

In spite of the fact that much of the area seems little altered by the passage of glacial ice, parts of the southern foothills are widely mantled with a layer of hummocky Laurentide till of variable thickness. This is especially the case throughout the landscape north and northeast of Waterton Lakes National Park, where the many small lakes occupy closed depressions in the till.

A number of investigators of glacial geology in the southern foothills have remarked upon the relative paucity of evidence of really effective erosional action by ice. A possible explanation of the seeming geomorphologic discrepency lies in the fact that continental ice in the Foothills Belt was at or near the extreme limit of its expansion, so that its rate of advance was probably slowed considerably along the outer margin. It also seems reasonable to suppose that ice near the edge of the glacier was relatively thin and probably stagnating and melting down in many places. Given these circumstances, it is perhaps not too surprising that gradational activity was apparently somewhat limited.

Another possibility accounting for the general lack of evidence of widespread and deep-seated glacial action in much of the area is that the Laurentide ice which reached the Rocky Mountain front did so very early in Pleistocene time; the more recent continental glaciers of the western Canadian plains may not have covered much of the Foothills Belt. If this were indeed the case, and several students of the region think it was, then most of the geomorphologic evidence of strong glacial activity could easily have been destroyed or significantly modified by later, non-glacial processes. Whatever the true state of affairs may have been, much of the modern landscape is dominated by forms indicating gradational alteration primarily by non-glacial forces, principally post-glacial streams and rivers.

The Foothills Erratics Train

One of the most intriguing landscape features of the outer Foothills Belt is the presence of scattered pinkish or purplish quartzite boulders in a comparatively narrow zone extending southeast from the latitude of Jasper National Park to beyond the international boundary; these constitute the so-called *Foothills Erratics Train.* The largest of the foothills erratics is the well-known *Big Rock* west of Okotoks *(Figure 48)*, but it is only one of literally tens of thousands of such blocks which are found in a 400-mile belt of irregular width roughly paralleling the Rocky Mountain front *(Figure 49)*.

The boulders are obviously erratics — they are of a rock type different from the underlying bedrock, which is usually

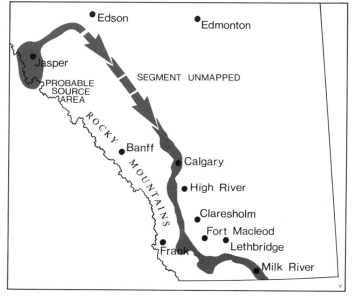

Figure 49. Map showing distribution of the boulders of the Foothills Erratics Train. Isolated boulders have been observed between Calgary and Edson, but detailed mapping has not been completed.

sandstone or shale. They attracted the attention of the first scientific observers of southwestern Alberta glacial geology in the 1880's and have been an object of study ever since. Most of the geologists who initially encountered the rocks of the Erratics Train reached the eminently logical conclusion that the boulders must have been moved and deposited by glacial ice; no other mode of transportation seems reasonably to

account for the widespread distribution of the blocks. There was disagreement, however, as to the source area for the pieces of quartzite, with some observers opting for the mountains in the Waterton area, while others proposed the Canadian Shield.

Figure 50. One of thousands of boulders in the Foothills Erratics Train; this one is located west of Fort Macleod. Weathering has caused it to split apart after deposition.

As the full sweep of the geographical extent of the erratics became known through careful mapping, it was apparent that the Waterton region could not have been the source. Geological investigations in the vicinity of Jasper have subsequently revealed the presence there of quartzitic rock of a type very similar to that in the Erratics Train. The distributional pattern of the boulders, elongated in a northwest-southeast belt, suggests transportation by ice moving toward the southeast through the outer Foothills Belt.

As presently envisioned by several investigators, the Foothills Erratics Train originated in late Pleistocene time when a landslide similar to but much smaller than the Frank Slide dropped several million tons of rock onto the surface of a glacier in the Athabasca Valley near the town of Jasper. This glacier carried the blocks of the fragmented slide out of the mountains and into the northern Foothills Belt. Somewhere between Hinton and Edson the Athabasca glacier was deflected toward the southeast by the edge of the Laurentide ice and forced to flow generally in that direction along the margin of the continental glacier. The boulders were deposited in their present pattern as movement ceased and stagnation and ultimate melting brought about disappearance of the glacier.

If seen only individually, the boulders of the Train *(Figure 50)* are confusing in their appearance and seemingly possess a haphazard, almost senseless distributional pattern. A full understanding of the geomorphologic implications of the scattered erratics requires knowledge of the very considerable length of the Train and its location in a narrow zone flanking the mountains. The Foothills Erratics Train is thus one of the more interesting facets of the Pleistocene geology of this part of the province, serving as a striking reminder of the effectiveness of glacial action in the making of the landscapes of southern Alberta.

The Porcupine Hills

Although topographically and geographically part of the general foothills region, the Porcupine Hills differ notably in geologic structure. A simplified cross-section will serve to make the point *(Figure 51)*. Quite unlike the "true" foothills to the west (see *Figure 43*), the Porcupines are underlain by only very gently dipping beds of sandstone and shale, making them much more akin to the plains in terms of fundamental

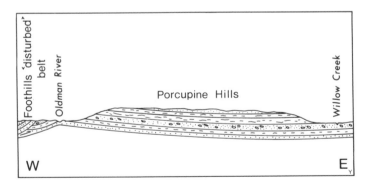

Figure 51. Diagrammatic cross-sectional sketch of the Porcupine Hills showing general structural characteristics. The gently dipping beds underlying the Hills differ notably from the folded and thrust-faulted strata of the "true" Foothills Belt.

Figure 52. Southwestern margin of the Porcupine Hills north of Pincher Station. Bedrock dips gently toward the east in this view, which faces north.

Figure 53. Southeastern flank of the Porcupine Hills west of Fort Macleod. The approximately horizontal attitude of the shale and sandstone beds is very apparent in this picture.

geology; the primary structural feature of the Hills is a broad, shallow syncline. Their basic characteristics are especially well displayed near the southwestern and southeastern margins *(Figures 52 and 53)*, where stratification in the bedrock foundation is readily recognizable.

The Porcupine Hills are high enough so that parts of the south-central segment (generally areas above about 5,300 feet in elevation) escaped continental glaciation. However, Laurentide ice moved into, around, and through the Hills from the north, east, and south, with glacial tongues wedging up the valleys of Trout and Willow creeks to spill over into the Oldman River catchment basin. Mountain ice flowing through the Gap of the Oldman River in the Livingstone Range brushed at least once against parts of the western flank of the Hills.

Figure 54. View looking into the northern end of "The Canyon" west of Claresholm.

One of the most striking indirect effects of glaciation in the Porcupine Hills was the formation of a series of large, deep, bedrock channels along parts of their eastern margin. West of Claresholm, Stavely, and Parkland, respectively, are "The Canyon", Boneyard Coulee, and Pine Coulee, all very impressive drainageways rather curiously perched on the side of the Hills and generally dry today *(Figures 54, 55, and 56)*. Customarily, we do not expect to find water-cut channels of these dimensions running *across* the edge of topographic

highlands; the usual situation is for such drainages to be oriented so as to conduct flow *down* the regional slope. How, then, to account for these rather unusual landscape features?

The explanation lies in a consideration of conditions along the eastern flank of the Porcupine Hills during the most recent period of deglaciation. As the margin of the Laurentide glacier melted back from and down the eastern flank, meltwater streams formed on the side of the Hills, forced to flow along and perhaps underneath the edge of the ice and confined by the slope of the land to the west *(Figure 57)*. The margin of the wasting ice must have been highly irregular, in conformity with the underlying terrain, and the sinuous meltwater streams, trapped between the glacier and the slope of the Hills, simply cut down in place, thus producing the large channels. As the ice surface lowered and its edge moved progressively farther eastward, successively lower channels were eroded (see *Figure 57*), and ultimately the modern Willow Creek drainage became established. The channels cut during a waning phase of the Ice Age remain isolated on the side of the Hills, their origin difficult to understand by reference only to the stream systems of the present. They are, in short, still another relic of the Ice Age, with which the landscapes of southern Alberta are abundantly blessed.

Figure 55. Boneyard Coulee west of Stavely.

Figure 56. Pine Coulee west of Parkland.

Figure 58. Foothills scene west of Nanton looking southwest toward the first of the Front Ranges.

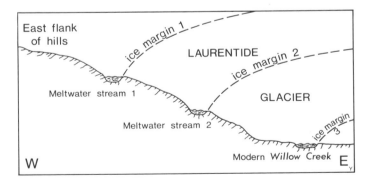

Figure 57. Sketch showing the probable origin of meltwater channels on the eastern slope of the Porcupine Hills. With ultimate disappearance of the Laurentide ice, the channels were left perched high and dry on the side of the hills; the modern drainage is concentrated in Willow Creek.

Figure 59. The southern Foothills Belt, with Leavitt in the middle ground and the Rockies of Glacier National Park on the skyline.

Figure 60. Foothills scene in the middle Castle River valley between Burmis and Beaver Mines. Peaks of the first of the Rocky Mountain Front Ranges dominate the skyline.

Summary

For many southern Albertans, the foothills are perhaps the most charming part of the province. From the rounded tree- and shrub-covered ridges in the north *(Figure 58)* to the rolling, grassy country of the south *(Figure 59)*, foothills landscapes offer a restful alternative to the vertical magnificence of the Rockies or the almost frightening vastness of the plains. Man's use (or mis-use) of the land has in a few places created a jarring and discordant note, but much of the Foothills Belt has been treated kindly and remains readily accessible to all *(Figure 60)*.

The intensity of operation of the geological and geomorphological agents of change has been considerably less here than in the adjacent mountains, and foothills landscapes clearly reflect this fact. Without worrying too much about underlying structural features, one can nevertheless appreciate the relationship between subsurface geologic processes (in this case, folding and thrust-faulting) and operation of the gradational forces at the earth's surface. Tectonic activity has been responsible for creation of the basic framework of the foothills, while running water and glaciers have modified but certainly not obscured the fundamental structural features. A land of gentle ridges and valleys, the Foothills Belt is one of the more attractive natural regions of southern Alberta.

CHAPTER 5
THE PLAINS

Superficially, the plains region of southern Alberta *(Figure 61)* may seem to be the simplest part of the province, at least in terms of geologic structure, and therefore of considerably less interest than the foothills or mountains. Such expressions as "those endless plains", "the monotonous prairies", "a vast, treeless expanse", and others of similar ilk have long created a mental image of physiographic sameness, leading to the conception of a landscape hopelessly flat and dull. Nothing could be farther from the truth — the area is amply supplied with unusual topographic features, most of which are a direct product of Laurentide glaciation and post-glacial activity by streams and the wind, and is certainly worthy of extended study.

Geologic Structure

It is obviously the case that the basic geology of the plains is much less complex than that of the foothills and Rocky Mountains. With but few exceptions, bedrock consists of many thousands of feet of sedimentary layers, all more or less horizontal (see *Figure 7,* Chapter 2). The structural situation here suggests a long period of accumulation of sediments (both marine and non-marine), interrupted by occasional episodes of epeirogenic uplift during which erosion replaced deposition as the primary gradational process in the region. Orogenic activity, leading to complex structures and major topographic highlands, has apparently been all but absent for hundreds of

Figure 61. The southern Alberta plains: Looking northwest from Milk River Ridge toward Lethbridge.

millions of years. The dominant process in the plains for the last 20-25 million years prior to Pleistocene glaciation was erosion, during which many hundreds of feet of sediments were stripped away by the pre-glacial streams of late Tertiary time.

Unlike the situation in the foothills and Front Ranges, bedrock in the plains is usually concealed, buried in most places by a veneer of glacial and post-glacial debris. Till constitutes the greater part of this covering layer, with an average thickness of perhaps 80-100 feet. As a general rule, the higher the topographic surface, the thinner the mantle of glacial and other unconsolidated materials. In the main, exposures of bedrock are limited to the walls of post-glacial valleys or to man-made excavations. Almost anywhere bedrock can be seen, the approximately horizontal layering is readily observable *(Figures 62 and 63),* from the edge of the Foothills Belt in the west all the way to the Saskatchewan border. The

Figure 63. Valley of the South Saskatchewan River near Redcliff. Horizontal layering in the beds of sandstone and shale is clearly visible.

Figure 62. Horizontally bedded sedimentary rocks along the Milk River just east of Whiskey Gap.

very gentle dips in bedrock imparted by the two subsurface structures mentioned in Chapter 2 (the Sweetgrass Arch and the Alberta Syncline) are usually not discernible in any single stream-bank exposure; their presence was detected by regional geologic mapping and measurements of dip over a wide area.

Two comparatively small areas within the plains province display structural characteristics indicative of deep-seated tectonic disturbance. Along the Oldman River south of Monarch there is a zone of fault blocks in bedrock (the *Monarch Disturbed Belt*) suggesting thrust-faulting of slices of the uppermost (youngest) formations. And in the upper Bullshead Creek drainage, northwest of the Cypress Hills, bedrock is highly disturbed, apparently as a result of faulting at depth. Faulting on a minor scale also offsets exposed bedrock formations in stream valleys in widely separated parts of the region, as illustrated by the small reverse fault in the St. Mary River valley shown in *Figure 6,* Chapter 2.

Nevertheless, the general structural pattern is simple — almost anywhere within the larger region, bedrock is upper

Cretaceous sandstone or shale of horizontal or only very gently dipping attitude. Younger rocks are found at higher elevations in the Cypress and Porcupine Hills, but the more recent formations have been eroded away to expose Cretaceous sediments over the greater part of the area. The structural scene, in short, is relatively uncomplicated, and diversity of surficial features depends primarily upon types and intensities of gradational processes.

General Evolution of the Modern Landscape

The earliest record of events culminating in development of the contemporary plains landscape can be traced back some 60-70 million years, when tectonic activity to the west produced the ancestral Rocky Mountain ranges. Withdrawal of the last major interior sea in western North America occurred at about that time, bringing to an end deposition of marine sediments in the region. With the rise of the ancient Rockies, there began a prolonged period of accumulation of a great blanket of terrestrial sediments over much of the plains region. These came from the mountains and were transported and deposited by numerous streams and rivers originating in the highlands. Deposition occurred intermittently for perhaps 30-35 million years, the result being the formation of thousands of feet of non-marine sedimentary rocks across most of the plains.

However, beginning about 25 million years ago, the dominant geomorphologic process became degradation, probably as a result of broad-scale uplift and tilting, and erosion by rivers originating in the western mountains has been more or less continuous since that time. Gradational lowering of the general plains surface has been uneven, as rivers have shifted their courses laterally and rocks of differing resistance have been encountered. As a result, parts of the southern plains stand well above the rest of the region; the Cypress Hills, Porcupine Hills, and Milk River Ridge are topographically higher primarily because of preservation from the effects of gradational lowering rather than as a result of structural, or tectonic, uplift. All of the more-elevated tracts were probably segments of pre-glacial stream divides and thus less subject to erosional destruction than adjacent parts of the plains.

Although glacial and other unconsolidated deposits overlie bedrock almost everywhere in southern Alberta, a reasonable reconstruction of the late-Tertiary, pre-glacial landscape has been made possible through study of literally thousands of logs from water, oil, and gas wells. The excellent record of subsurface conditions contained in these logs indicates that the landscape prior to Pleistocene glaciation was a rolling one, with integrated stream systems flowing in broad valleys separated by rounded bedrock divides. Total relief was probably somewhat greater than that of the present, with interfluvial ridges standing 350-400 feet above valley floors. The pre-glacial regional drainage was generally toward the northeast, resembling the modern stream pattern in gross form, although not in detail.

Laurentide glacial ice moved across the area a number of times during the Pleistocene Epoch, mainly from the north, northeast, and east. The latest glacial movement through much of southern Alberta appears to have been toward the

Figure 64. Cliff along the Oldman River south of Kipp. At least three layers of till are present in this exposure, one of the most spectacular in southern Alberta.

southeast, with ice crossing the international boundary and extending well into north-central Montana. There is no general agreement among investigators as to the number of advances and retreats or the age of the earliest of the continental glaciations. Published accounts of glacial stratigraphy mention the occurrence of from as few as two or three to as many as five or six separate advances. Estimates of the age of the oldest of these range from early Pleistocene (perhaps 2.5-3 million years ago) to the period of the most recent major glaciation (known in mid-continental North America as the Wisconsin) some 70,000 to 12,000-15,000 years ago.

Figure 65. Glacial till (light-colored) on top of bedrock, St. Mary River valley south of Lethbridge. The sharp surface of separation between bedrock and the overlying till is apparent, as is the tendency for the till to stand vertically in such exposures.

Evidence of the number and age of glaciations comes from bluffs along the major rivers *(Figure 64)*, where several distinct sheets of till, separated by non-glacial sediments, may be discerned. The planes of separation between till layers and non-glacial deposits are sharp and readily recognizable in most places *(Figure 65)*. There is no problem in identifying the oldest till present in such exposures — the Principle of

Superposition (Chapter 3) tells us that the one at the bottom must have been deposited before the others. Differences and disputations arise concerning the precise *age* of the lowest till, and these, as indicated, have not yet been settled.

However, resolution of the problem of how many glaciations affected the plains of southern Alberta (and exactly *when*) is not absolutely critical to an understanding of the origin of the modern landscape. Suffice it to remark that *several* advances of continental ice occurred in the region, the most recent of which began its final retreat perhaps 12,000-15,000 years ago. The landscape of the present is thus a very young one, "young", at least, as geologists measure time.

Contrary to some popular opinion, the overall geomorphologic effects of continental glaciation in the plains appear not to have been especially dramatic. Probably the most significant modification was a smoothing out, or levelling up, of the topography, largely as a result of the filling in of pre-glacial valleys with till and other debris. There is little evidence to suggest that interstream uplands were eroded intensively. In terms of gross physiographic change, then, a landscape of broad river valleys and well-defined interfluvial divides, with a total relief of several hundred feet, was converted to one of much more even surface configuration and considerably less relief.

Although the precise details of deglaciation in the plains will never be known completely, the general pattern of events seems reasonably clear. Basing their estimates on geomorphologic evidence and a limited number of radiocarbon (C_{14}) dates, several investigators have concluded that this part of North America must have been ice-free by 10,000-12,000 years ago. As the continental ice sheet waned, its margin retreating toward the east and northeast, initiation and elaboration of the modern stream systems began. Locations and rates of downcutting of the late- and post-glacial rivers were conditioned by at least three factors: (1) Initial irregularities and general easterly to northeasterly slope of the emerging land surface; (2) relative resistance of earth materials encountered by the youthful streams; and (3) position of the receding (or stagnating) ice front. It seems probable that the contemporary rivers had attained essentially their present locations across the region by some 6,000-8,000 years ago; deepening of their valleys has been the primary geomorphologic activity since that time. In places, the modern drainages follow segments of pre-glacial channels; in others, the post-glacial valleys are in new courses.

This thumbnail sketch of the general sequence of geologic events leading to the modern landscape will serve as an

Figure 66. Rolling till-plain topography northeast of Manyberries.

introduction to discussions of specific aspects of the regional geomorphology, almost all of which are related, in one way or another, to late- and post-glacial gradational activity. As noted above, the landscape is young, and land forms of late- and post-glacial age are still fresh enough that their origin, in most cases, is readily understandable. As will be seen, there is an amazing diversity of forms in the seemingly "simple" plains. Topographic monotony may prevail on a sub-continental scale or in comparison with the more rugged Rockies, but in detail the landscape is far from being the uncomplicated surface it appears to some.

Details of the Plains Landscape
There is no necessarily obvious or inherently logical order in which to consider the many "special" physiographic features of the plains of southern Alberta. Ideally, they should probably be discussed in the chronological order in which they evolved in post-glacial time, but our knowledge of this matter is far too limited to permit such an approach. The *gross* character of the landscape has been strongly conditioned and controlled by Laurentide glaciation, and if a blindfolded

person were to stick a pin into a map of the southern plains, the chances are good the pin would strike an area with glacial debris (most likely till) at the surface. A reasonably safe generalization, then, is that much of the landscape consists of rolling, hummocky till plain *(Figures 66, 67, and 68)*, underlain by a mantle of debris of variable thickness deposited directly from glacial ice. In most places, close examination of a fresh exposure would reveal several sheets of till, indicating the occurrence of more than one episode of continental glaciation. The till would be seen to consist of a heterogeneous, non-bedded mixture of rock material of all sizes, with occasional erratics (mostly igneous and metamorphic rocks from the Canadian Shield) and finer particles (mostly of more local origin) jumbled together in disorderly fashion. In many exposures there is a pronounced tendency for the till to stand almost vertically (see *Figure 65*); this condition arises from the presence in some till sheets of vertical joints or fissures along which the material weathers and sloughs off.

Fortunately (or so it seems to the author), the overall landscape of our "reasonably safe generalization" is varied and diversified by a number of most interesting subsidiary forms, and these will be described below. The order in which they are discussed should not be taken to indicate the author's idea of their relative importance; they are *all* important.

Figure 67. Cultivated hummocky moraine southwest of Wrentham.

Figure 68. Rolling, hummocky till plain east of Iddesleigh.

Channels in the Plains

As the margin of the most recent continental glacier in southern Alberta stagnated and eventually began to recede toward the east and northeast, there came into existence a number of extensive but short-lived *proglacial lakes,* relatively shallow bodies of water fed mainly by the melting ice mass and ponded between its edge and higher ground to the west. Their relationship to the landscape of the present rests upon the facts that (1) fine-grained sediments (mostly silts and clays) were deposited on their beds, giving rise to areas of relatively flat topography, and (2) they were systematically drained by a series of channels in which runoff ultimately reached the Milk and Missouri rivers; most of these channels — the large coulees of the prairies — are dry today.

The sequence of inter-related events leading to contemporary conditions can best be visualized with the aid of *Figure 69,* which shows the major late- and immediately post-glacial channels, as well as the modern rivers. As the Laurentide glacier began to retreat from its westernmost position near the mountains, meltwater from the continental ice and runoff from the Rockies were forced to flow south by way of a series of channels cut through the western end of Milk River Ridge (the continuation of which across the international boundary is known as *Hudson Bay Divide).* The largest of these is *Whiskey Gap (Figure 70),* through which water from the north and northwest was led into the upper reaches of the ancestral Milk River system. Sizable lakes evidently did not form along the southern margin of the Rockies at this time; runoff from the wasting Laurentide glacier (plus that provided by Rocky Mountain streams) must have followed innumerable and shifting channels between the ice margin and the Front Ranges, all eventually funneling through Whiskey Gap and other breaks in Milk River Ridge and the Hudson Bay Divide.

With the passage of time, the edge of the continental ice moved eastward and northeastward, and a large lake formed in the general vicinity of Magrath, north of central Milk River Ridge. This temporary water body was drained south across the Ridge and into the Milk River through *Lonely Valley (Figure 71).* Further retreat of the ice margin allowed the surface of the lake to lower and runoff to flow around the northern flank of Milk River Ridge by way of *Middle* and *Kipp coulees (Figures 72 and 73)* and then into *Verdigris Coulee (Figure 74),* once again spilling into the Milk River system east of Milk River town.

Continued northeasterly recession of the Laurentide glacier brought into existence *Etzikom Coulee (Figures 75 and 76)* and later *Chin Coulee (Figures 77 and 78),* the latter joined near its eastern end by *Forty Mile Coulee (Figure 79).* At this time there was probably an extensive lake in the area between Lethbridge and Taber; deposition of horizontal layers of fine sediment on its bed accounts for the remarkable flatness of terrain between these two communities.

So long as the continental ice blocked a runoff route around the north side of the Cypress Hills, all of the discharge originating to the west and flowing in the Etzikom-Chin-Forty Mile coulee systems was directed into the basin of Pakowki Lake (see *Figure 69)* and then south into the Milk River by way of *Pakowki* or *Pendant d'Oreille Coulee (Figure 80).* Although the basin is essentially dry today, the Pakowki Lake of that time must have been a sizable, though shallow, body of water.

As the retreating margin of the continental glacier eventually cleared the Cypress Hills, drainage became possible around the northern side of this barrier, and runoff from the combined Chin-Forty Mile system cut *Seven Persons Coulee (Figure 81).* Additionally, the broad channel east of Medicine Hat occupied by the Trans-Canada Highway and the Canadian Pacific mainline was evidently eroded by east-flowing meltwater when the ice margin lay immediately to the north.

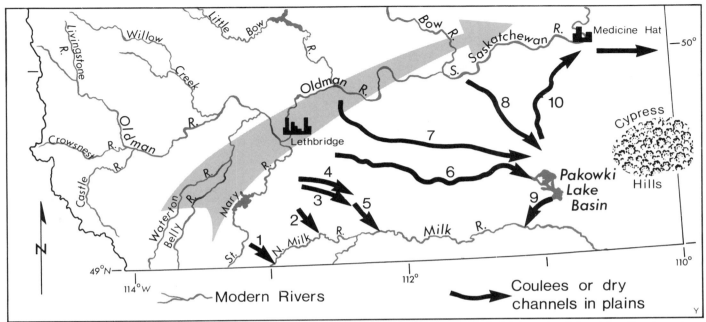

Figure 69. Modern stream systems of southern Alberta and the late-glacial and immediately post-glacial channels of the plains. Dry channels and coulees discussed in the text are numbered as follows: 1. *Whiskey Gap* 2 . *Lonely Valley.* 3. *Middle Coulee.* 4. *Kipp Coulee.* 5. *Verdigris Coulee.* 6. *Etzikom Coulee.* 7. *Chin Coulee.* 8. *Forty Mile Coulee.* 9. *Pakowki (Pendant d'Oreille) Coulee.* 10. *Seven Persons Coulee.* Large arrow indicates general direction of retreat of ice margin.

Ultimately, the Laurentide glacier receded into and beyond what was to become Saskatchewan, and the modern South Saskatchewan River of southern Alberta was formed.

The legacy of the most recent period of deglaciation in southern Alberta thus includes the rather unusual coulees, which seem to originate in no particular place and to wander rather aimlessly across the prairie, and largish areas of lake bed topography, conspicuous by virtue of their comparative flatness in contrast to the rolling terrain of much of the region *(Figures 82 and 83).* And finally, there is perhaps the single most spectacular landscape feature in this part of the province, the canyon of the Milk River through the last 15-20 miles of its course in southern Alberta *(Figure 84).* The *size* of the canyon just doesn't seem to make sense in terms of the river's modern drainage area and discharge. The Milk River of today

is a good example of what geomorphologists call an *underfit stream* — its valley seems much too big to have been eroded by runoff of the present, and at some time in the past, presumably, total flow in the stream system must have been greater. This appears precisely to have been the case: Most canyon cutting took place when virtually all of the runoff from southwestern Alberta was being diverted into the Milk River as a result of blockage by ice of drainage to the northeast. With recession of the Laurentide glacier out of the region and opening of a route around the Cypress Hills, evolution of the modern South Saskatchewan drainage began, and waters that previously were feeding the Milk River became incorporated into the Hudson Bay catchment basin. Sustained only by runoff originating mainly in the western plains, the modern Milk River seems strangely out of place in the broad, deep canyon it now occupies.

Figure 70. Whiskey Gap. The view is from the south side of this dry valley and looks northeast. Drainage in late glacial time was from left to right.

Figure 72. Aerial view of Middle Coulee looking due east over the eastern end of Milk River Ridge Reservoir.

Figure 71. Lonely Valley, cutting across Milk River Ridge south of Magrath. Low-altitude aerial view (on a hazy day) looking slightly east of north. Drainage was toward the lower right-hand corner of the photo.

Figure 73. Ground view of Middle Coulee east of Milk River Ridge Reservoir; the view is toward the west.

Figure 74. Lower Verdigris Coulee as seen from east of Milk River town. West Butte of the Sweetgrass Hills is on the skyline.

Figure 76. Looking east in Etzikom Coulee from south of Wrentham.

Figure 75. Middle segment of Etzikom Coulee; looking west from an elevation of about 1,000 feet.

Figure 77. Mid-winter view of Chin Coulee south of Taber; view is toward the west.

69

Figure 78. Chin Coulee north of Foremost as seen from the ground. Drainage was from right to left.

Figure 80. Pakowki Coulee, by which water was drained from the basin of Lake Pakowki into the Milk River system. West Butte of the Sweetgrass Hills is on the horizon.

Figure 79. Aerial view of lower Forty Mile Coulee near its junction with Chin Coulee.

Figure 81. Beginning of Seven Persons Coulee, formed by the junction of Chin (lower right) and Forty Mile (centre left) coulees north of Etzikom.

Studied in isolation and without regard for the effects of deglaciation, the large coulees of the southern Alberta plains would remain a somewhat mysterious element in the prairie landscape, their origin far from clear to many observers. The temptation might be strong to postulate the occurrence of some brief, catastrophic geologic or climatic incident in order to explain ·their presence. As it is, resort to tectonic or meteorologic violence is unnecessary — formation of these impressive drainageways and enlargement of the Milk River canyon were logical consequences of the availability of a substantial volume of meltwater that had to go *somewhere* and was sure to cut impressive channels as it flowed across the

Figure 83. Lake-bed topography north of Welling. View is toward the southeast and Milk River Ridge is on the skyline.

Figure 82. Very flat lake-bed terrain south of Foremost.

regional surface. The area is physiographically richer for the presence of these most interesting features, and they provide still further evidence of the direct and indirect importance of glaciation to an understanding of landscape evolution in our part of the world.

The Wind

Three elements (or aspects) of the plains landscape can be attributed, in one way or another, to gradational action by the wind. These are: (1) A number of interesting dune areas; (2) the geographical distribution of post-glacial landslides of the slump variety; and (3) the remarkable pattern of alignment of small coulees in an area extending roughly from Lethbridge west to the mountains. The degree of direct wind control in the evolution of these features appears to vary from case to case, but there is little doubt about its involvement in each.

Dunes. There are four well-defined clusters of elongated dunes in southern Alberta, all lying within the zone of strongest, most persistent southwesterly winds, the so-called *Chinook Belt.* Long, narrow dunes (known technically as *longitudinal dunes*, the long axes of which parallel the effective wind) are found (1) southeast of Lake Newell, between the reservoir and the town of Rolling Hills, (2) east of Carmangay, in a belt extending from Highway 23 to Travers Reservoir, (3) northeast of Purple Springs, between Highway 3 and the Oldman River, and (4) in a triangular piece of land southwest of Monarch bounded

Figure 84. Looking west into the deepest part of the Milk River Canyon (400-450 feet) south of Comrey.

the Oldman and Belly rivers. Additionally, the Middle Sand Hills north of Medicine Hat are part of a much larger area of discontinuous dune fields extending well into southwestern Saskatchewan.

The four clusters of longitudinal dunes listed above are all similar in that they display a consistent northeast-southwest alignment; this pattern strongly suggests an origin related to prevailing southwesterly winds in post-glacial time. The pattern of alignment is not very striking as viewed from the ground, but aerial views *(Figures 85 and 86)* clearly reveal the linear nature of the accumulations of wind-blown materials and their general NE-SW orientation in the landscape.

The story of the development of these isolated dune fields seems clear: They represent surficial materials transported and deposited by strong southwesterly winds at a time when the natural vegetation of the southern plains was sparser than it is today and thus was providing less protection against wind erosion. A reasonable assumption is that they were formed not too long after disappearance of Laurentide ice from the areas in which they are located. Source areas for the dune sediments

may well have been the dry beds of former proglacial lakes, on which the presence of fine-grained sediments susceptible to wind action would be expected. With the establishment of a post-glacial cover of grass over most of the region, the effectiveness of the wind as a direct gradational agent has been considerably reduced, and stabilization of the dunes has taken place.

Landslides. A second piece of evidence suggestive of the indirect role of the wind in landscape evolution and alteration is represented by the distribution of post-glacial landslides in the plains of southern Alberta. A study by the author four years ago discovered that of more than 100 slump-type landslides identified, most of which are along the valleys of the major rivers *(Figures 87 and 88)*, three-fourths (75 percent) are on slopes facing north, northeast, or east. The situation in the vicinity of Lethbridge is instructive in this regard. *Figure 89* shows the location of a number of large slumps along the

Oldman and St. Mary rivers in and near the city, and their concentration on the indicated slopes is notable, with most located on the west sides of the rivers. The material involved in these slumps is largely till, although a few consist in part of bedrock.

Other things being equal (which they rarely are in the real world), one would expect the areal distribution of such landslides to be more or less even across the landscape. On the other hand, if undercutting of steep banks by stream action were the primary cause of slumping, then the slides would presumably be found mainly on the outsides of curves or meanders along the prairie rivers. However, this is conspicuously not the case, and the pronounced tendency for slumping to occur on slopes of particular aspect suggests control by some other factor. Prevailing winds, especially during periods of strong Chinooks, are believed to be that "other factor". Strong winds appear to have influenced the location of slumping primarily through their role in distributing snow unequally across the prairie surface, with large drifts customarily building up on the leeward (downwind) slopes. Since the strongest winds are southwesterly, major accumulations of snow tend to develop on east-, northeast-, and north-facing slopes, and it is on just these exposures that a majority of the post-glacial landslides have occurred.

Engineers and geologists are in agreement that soil moisture content is critical in the evolution of several types of mass movement, including many landslides. Generally speaking, the wetter the soil, the greater its degree of instability and potential for movement. Slopes on which large snowdrifts normally accumulate are assured of a greater moisture supply, whatever the nature of the surficial materials or underlying bedrock may be, and accordingly are more likely to undergo mass movement of one sort or another.

Figure 85. Large dunes (arrows) between Monarch and Pearce south of Highway 3. The view is slightly east of south, and the stream in the background is the Belly River.

Figure 86. Elongated dunes (arrow) along the south side of the Oldman River northeast of Purple Springs. The view is slightly south of east.

Figure 87. Slump-type landslide on west bank of Oldman River in West Lethbridge.

Figure 88. Active slumping (since 1961) in an abandoned meander of the St. Mary River about 15 miles south of Lethbridge.

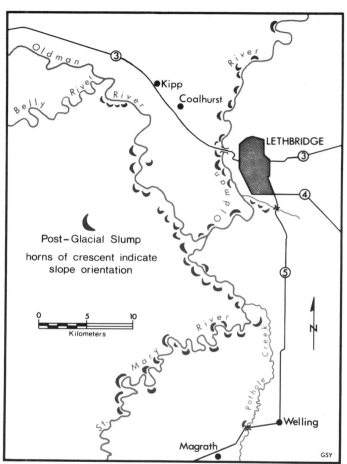

Figure 89. Map showing slumps along the Oldman and St. Mary rivers near Lethbridge. These were first tentatively identified on aerial photographs and then confirmed by field checks.

Distribution of landslides in the southern plains thus appears to have been affected, to a large degree, by moisture availability, and this, in turn, has been controlled by the wind. The wettest slopes during post-glacial time have sustained the greatest number of slumps, and the rather curious distributional pattern of slumping is thereby satisfactorily explained.

Coulee Alignment. Finally, mention should be made of still another landscape feature believed to be related to effective wind action. This is the notable development of parallel alignment in small coulees tributary to the major streams from Lethbridge west to the Rocky Mountain front. Virtually all of the larger valleys in the plains have short, steep tributaries, but the pattern of alignment of these is significantly different in different parts of the region. East of Lethbridge, most smaller

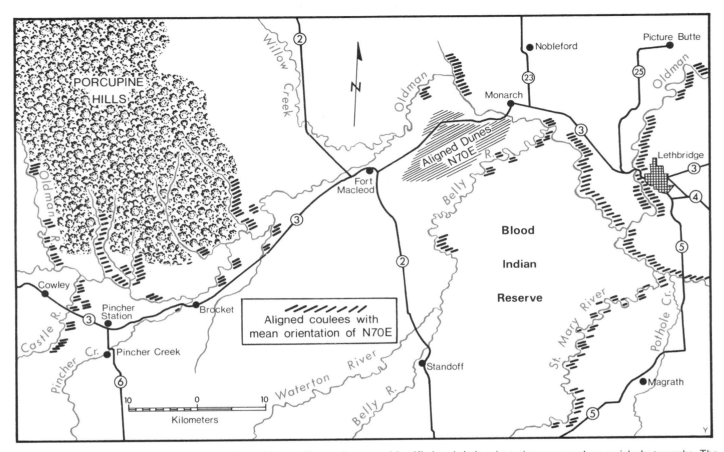

Figure 90. Location of aligned coulees in southern Alberta. The coulees were identified and their orientation measured on aerial photographs. The size of the coulees has been exaggerated for cartographic clarity.

coulees are oriented approximately at right angles to the general valley trends, suggesting that they have been cut by surface runoff taking the most direct route down the valley walls. But in a zone extending from that city to the mountains, a decidedly preferred alignment is evident in many clusters of coulees along segments of the Oldman, St. Mary, Belly, and Castle rivers, as well as on several smaller streams on the southern flanks of the Porcupine Hills *(Figure 90).* The mean trend of more than 250 such coulees is $70°$ east of north (they have a *strike* of N70E, or an *azimuth* of 070), and most

of them are on valley walls with a southwesterly, or *windward,* exposure. As observed from the ground, the parallel alignment of the coulees is scarcely detectable, but low-altitude aerial views dramatically illustrate the spectacular pattern *(Figures 91, 92 and 93).*

How can we explain the restricted geographical distribution and strongly preferred alignment of these coulees? Many geologists have suggested that relatively straight topographic features at the surface of the earth (which are known as *linears* or *lineaments*) are a reflection of structural features in bedrock

Figure 91. Aligned coulees along the east side of the Oldman River north of Lethbridge. View is toward the northeast.

Figure 92. Cluster of coulees along the Castle River between Pincher Station and Cowley. Highway 3 shows in lower right corner.

(mainly joints and faults) beneath a veneer of unconsolidated materials. In some parts of the earth, subsurface structural characteristics undoubtedly control surface topography, but such an explanation for the aligned coulees of southern Alberta seems inadequate. If faults or other fissures in bedrock (which are known to be widely present in the prairies) were responsible for the pattern of coulee development here, then it would be reasonable to expect that parallel coulees of particular orientation should be found throughout *all* of the larger area. Furthermore, the location of coulees with respect to windward or leeward slopes would presumably be random. Neither condition is fulfilled in the southern plains. The aligned coulees have a limited geographical distribution, and most tend to occur on windward valley walls.

Without going into the minute details of the argument, it seems probable that the distribution and pattern of alignment of the parallel coulees can best be explained by reference to the wind. In a recently published study, the author proposed the following model of origin:

1. By 6,000-8,000 years ago the master streams of the southern plains were in approximately their present locations, and deepening of their youthful valleys had created sufficient relief for initiation of coulee development.

Figure 93. Coulees along the Oldman River north of Pincher Station. View is toward the southeast.

2. Windward topographic surfaces within the Chinook Belt are (and were) affected in at least two ways by strong southwesterly winds: (a) They retain less snow than other slopes in the region, and (b) their microclimate (the climate within a few inches of the surface) is considerably drier than that of the lee slopes (because of direct exposure to strong winds and solar radiation), leading to a significantly lesser vegetation cover. As a result, such surfaces are more susceptible to erosion.

3. Accordingly, on many of the southwesterly facing valley walls, wind-driven snow and rain differentially carved narrow, shallow, elongated surficial furrows that were later enlarged by surface runoff; the orientation of such furrows, in line with the strongest winds, determined the ultimate pattern attained by the aligned coulees. The process is thought to have been most effective during Fall and Winter when (a) the strongest Chinook winds blow, (b) many of the windward slopes are unfrozen and free from snow from time to time, and (c) the limited vegetation cover is dead or dormant, thus offering minimal protection against surface disturbance.

4. With the occasional summer thunderstorm providing most of the runoff, erosional deepening and lengthening of the furrows converted them from inconsequential initial forms to recognizable, growing drainage systems. Some material may have been deflated (blown) from walls and floors by the wind, but coulee enlargement was accomplished primarily by the erosional work of running water.

Although the evolutionary sequence of coulee development and alignment outlined above is not accepted by all students of the region, it does appear to account in a reasonably satisfactory way for the three outstanding characteristics of the coulees: (1) Their limited rather than universal geographical distribution, (2) their mean orientation of N70E (which parallels the direction of the strongest, most persistent winds), and (3) their locations predominantly on windward topographic surfaces. No other theory of origin is known that can explain *all* of the observed facts.

Acting as a gradational agent, the wind on the plains in post-glacial time has thus functioned, directly or indirectly, to produce a rather interesting suite of land forms. None of these is particularly massive or scenically overwhelming, but all are sufficiently different from other features of the modern landscape to warrant special consideration.

Figure 94. Badlands along the Red Deer River in Dinosaur Provincial Park.

Badlands

Prominently developed along segments of some of the rivers in the southern plains are extensive areas of so-called *badlands topography.* The term "badlands" was evidently first used in North America by early French trappers and traders who described the "mauvaises terres" of the White River in what is now the American state of South Dakota. Similar landscapes were subsequently encountered in other parts of the continent, including southern Alberta, and are now known to be restricted mainly to areas of arid to semi-arid climate in which relatively weak bedrock is horizontally layered and the vegetation cover extremely sparse or completely absent.

In our region, the badlands of the Red Deer River, spectacularly on display in Dinosaur Provincial Park *(Figure 94),* are probably best known, but comparable topography is also present in the extreme southeastern part of the province along the Lost River *(Figure 95)* and the Milk River Canyon *(Figure 96),* as well as in the Belly River Buttes northeast of Standoff.

Figure 95. Badlands along the Lost River near One Four in southeastern Alberta.

Figure 96. Badlands development along the Milk River canyon south of Comrey. The Sweetgrass Hills of Montana are in the background.

A typical tract of badlands consists of rough, intricate, narrowly and steeply gullied topography in which a continuous soil cover and plant life are all but missing; bedrock structure, in the form of horizontal bands of different colors and textures, is usually very apparent (see *Figure 94*). A visual impression of extremely rapid erosion prevails, and measurements of rates of slope retreat in Alberta and elsewhere (amounting to ½-¾ inch/year in the Red Deer valley, which is almost unbelieveably fast by geologic standards) confirm, in many instances, what the eye suggests. Most badlands development in the southern plains has been in rocks of the Oldman formation of Late Cretaceous age (see *Table II-A*, Chapter 2); this bedrock unit consists of alternating layers of non-marine sandstones and shales, with coal seams and scattered dinosaur fossils in its upper part. There seems to be an indirect relationship between thickness of till above bedrock and degree of evolution of badlands; the most complex badlands topography is found in areas with only a thin layer of glacial debris, while little or no badlands development has taken place where bedrock is buried by many tens of feet of till.

Careful studies of badlands formation and alteration in Dinosaur Provincial Park have established the fact that steep slopes in such terrain tend to be worn back approximately parallel to themselves; as the slopes recede toward drainage divides, they are being replaced at their bases by surfaces of lesser inclination, so-called *pediments (Figure 97)*. The exact mechanism of slope retreat is not completely understood, but weathering apparently loosens a thin, uniform sheet of material that can easily be eroded and transported during the occasional periods of surface runoff. With summer thunderstorms providing most of the runoff, the slopes are literally being peeled away, slice by slice. The rapidity of the process (by geologic standards) is such that soil development and establishment of a plant cover are strongly inhibited under existing climatic conditions. It seems probable that badlands evolution will be a continuing process of landscape change in parts of southern Alberta for an indeterminate period into the future.

The Cypress Hills

On July 28, 1859, Captain John Palliser wrote in his journal: "These hills [the Cypress Hills] are a perfect oasis in the desert we have travelled". Anyone who has thankfully climbed from the plains to the top of the Hills on a blistering midsummer afternoon can appreciate Palliser's thoughts about the area; the increased elevation of the plateau surface is great enough to make a significant difference in warm-season temperatures. Since Palliser's time, the Cypress Hills have been a region of considerable interest to all residents of and visitors to the southern Alberta and Saskatchewan prairies — they are "different" enough from the surrounding plains to have long attracted attention.

So far as basic geologic character is concerned, the Hills differ from the adjacent landscape mainly in the fact that their underlying bedrock layers (which are nearly horizontal, dipping only very slightly to the east) have been less intensively eroded and therefore stand higher than those of other parts of the plains. Capping the summit surface is a formation known as the Cypress Hills conglomerate, a mass of rounded pebbles and cobbles of variable thickness carried eastward in early and middle Tertiary time by streams originating in the ancient Rockies. During the prolonged period of erosional lowering of the general plains surface mentioned earlier in this chapter, the area that was to become the Cypress Hills was evidently a drainage divide separating the ancestral Saskatchewan and Missouri river systems. It seems probable that the Hills region has been a recognizable topographic eminence throughout much of the last 15-20 million years.

Figure 98. Low-altitude aerial view of west end of Cypress Hills; the Sweetgrass Hills are on the horizon. The rolling, disorganized landscape in the foreground consists of a great mass of glacial till deposited probably during the most recent episode of deglaciation in the region.

The physical features of the Cypress Hills area were modified during the Ice Age. At the beginning of the Pleistocene Epoch, the Hills themselves were part of a major watershed extending northeast from the Sweetgrass Hills of Montana; very little of southeastern Alberta was in the drainage basin of the Missouri River at that time. Glacial ice advanced toward and around the Hills several times; five separate sheets of till within a radius of 20 miles of the Hills are identified in a recently reported study. Ice seems to have moved generally toward the south in the area, although it was deflected toward the southeast around the western end. Ice lapped against the northern side of the Hills to an elevation of about 4,500 feet but reached elevations of several hundred feet less on the southern flank. Accordingly, about 80 square miles of the Alberta portion of the Hills remained unglaciated,

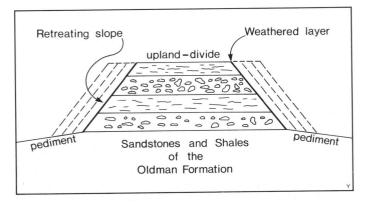

Figure 97. Diagrammatic representation of badlands slope retreat. The steep slopes retreat as weathering loosens and surface wash removes thin, uniform layers of rock material, and a new slope, the *pediment*, emerges at the toe of the steep escarpment. In time, the upland divide will be converted from a flat surface to a knife-edged ridge as the two retreating slopes meet.

Figure 99. West end of the Cypress Hills summit plateau; the view looks toward the east. "Head of the Mountain," the highest point in the Hills at 4,807 feet, is nearby.

standing as an elongated, flat-topped nunatak in the surrounding glacial "sea".

Impressive meltwater channels were eroded along the northern and western margins, leaving parts of these escarpments steep and sharply defined; the southern slopes are generally much less rugged. As deglaciation proceeded, large volumes of till accumulated along the northern side of the Hills, resulting in the creation of a hummocky, disorganized landscape that is particularly striking as seen from the air *(Figure 98)*. The main northern route into the Hills on Highway 48 leads through this region, the topography of which becomes conspicuously more irregular as Elkwater Lake is approached.

The summit and parts of the southern slopes are covered by a layer of wind-blown material known as *loess*. This consists of a mantle of fine-grained sediment varying in thickness from less than a foot to 6-8 feet; the extent of the loess veneer roughly corresponds to the unglaciated portion of the Hills. Since parts of the layer of loess have been deformed by frost action at some time in the past, it is assumed that its accumulation and disruption by frost heaving must have taken place during a period of cold, windy climatic conditions, possibly at or near the beginning of retreat of the latest Laurentide glacier.

Relatively little alteration of most of the Cypress Hills landscape appears to have occurred in post-glacial time. Under existing conditions, the remarkably flat plateau surface *(Figure 99)* seems virtually immune to erosional change throughout most of its extent. On the other hand, large-scale slumping has developed at places along the northern and western flanks. Elkwater Lake, for example, is dammed by a landslide at its western end, and a series of slump blocks is clearly visible from the viewpoint near the fire tower. The steepness of many segments of the northern margin *(Figure 100)* is directly attributable to widespread slumping thereon. In marked contrast, most of the slopes on the more gentle southern flank appear to have suffered little or no gradational alteration of consequence since withdrawal of the last continental ice sheet.

To many, the Cypress Hills represent something of an anomaly in the landscape of the southern plains. Ironically, they occupy a position near the centre of "Palliser's Triangle", a region of very low precipitation in southeastern Alberta and southwestern Saskatchewan once believed to be of little or no use to potential European settlers. It is the greater elevation of the Hills, rising as they do some 1,500-2,500 feet above the adjacent plains, that accounts for their seeming uniqueness. Temperatures are lower and precipitation is greater, so that

Figure 100. Steep slopes along the northern margin of the Cypress Hills. Slumping of the uppermost layers toward the left (north) has created the precipitous break in slope.

forest (lodgepole pine, white spruce, poplar) rather than grasses makes up much of the vegetation cover. Although the landscape scarcely suggests it, the highest point in the Hills, known as "Head of the Mountain" and situated near the western end of the plateau, is (at 4,807 feet) the greatest elevation in continental Canada between the mountains of the Labrador coast and the foothills of the Rockies. In reality, then, there is nothing especially "unusual" or "mysterious" about the natural environment of the Cypress Hills — after all, given sufficient elevation even parts of Hell would presumably become tolerable.

Hoodoos
along the Milk River

Although not a major element in the landscape of the southern plains, the so-called *hoodoos* of the Milk River, most easily seen in Writing-on-Stone Provincial Park, are an interesting example of the effects of weathering and erosion in rocks of differential resistance to gradational change. The inner valley of the river through the park is cut in an upper Cretaceous rock formation known as the Milk River sandstone (specifically, the lower member of that formation), and it is in this unit that hoodoos are most prominently developed *(Figure 101)*. The lower Milk River formation consists mostly of a greyish-to-whitish sandstone, interbedded with thin sheets of shale and often containing abundant *ironstone concretions.* The latter are simply tabular masses of sandstone in which iron compounds have been concentrated, principally by chemical action after deposition of the original rock. The concretions tend to be darker than the enclosing sandstone and, more importantly in the present context, significantly harder and thus more resistant to gradational alteration.

The first scientific study of the area was carried out by the geologist George M. Dawson in the 1870's. Dawson, one of the pioneering investigators of the geology of the western plains, described what is now called the Milk River formation as the

Figure 101. Milk River valley in Writing-on-Stone Provincial Park as seen from the north rim. Hoodoo development is most spectacular in the lower member of the Milk River sandstone, which forms the walls of the inner valley.

Figure 102. Hoodoos in Writing-on-Stone Provincial Park. The columns of light-grey sandstone are topped by thin layers of ironstone, which protect the weaker underlying rock material.

"castellated sandstones", in reference to the bizarre, castellated shapes of the outcrops along the Milk River. The rather unusual appearance of parts of the valley has since been commented upon by almost all observers in the region, and several fairly strange ideas about the formation of hoodoos have been proposed, most of which are wrong.

Actually, the origin of hoodoos seems to be a reasonably straightforward process, dependent primarily upon the characteristics of the rocks in which they develop and the nature of the regional climate. Close examination of the Milk River hoodoos will show that most consist of columns of light-colored rock capped by a relatively thin layer of darker rock *(Figure 102)*; the cap is usually a piece of ironstone. What has happened along the Milk River valley is simply that as the river cut down through the Milk River formation, weathering and erosion by running water and wind have more effectively eaten away the softer, lighter-colored sandstone, leaving the columns of weaker rock capped and protected by masses of the harder ironstone. The climate of the area is semi-arid, with infrequent summer thunderstorms, so that soil formation and establishment of a plant cover can proceed only very slowly under existing conditions. Hoodoos can thus be considered a special feature of badlands topographic evolution, most spectacularly developed in bedrock formations similar to the Milk River sandstone.

A formal definition of a hoodoo, taken from the American Geological Institute's *Glossary of Geology*, reads as follows: "A fantastic column, pinnacle, or pillar of rock produced in a region of sporadic heavy rainfall by differential weathering or erosion of horizontal strata, facilitated by joints and by layers of varying hardness, and occurring in varied and often eccentric or grotesque forms." The hoodoos of the Milk River conform almost perfectly to the technical description and provide another "special" geomorphologic feature in the regional landscape.

Prairie Mounds

A strange, almost esoteric land form is present in large numbers throughout a wide area in the southern Alberta plains, yet probably most residents of the region are totally unaware of its existence. This is the enigmatic *prairie mound,* a low, circular or oval mound with a central depression, sizable

Figure 103. Prairie mounds east of Seven Persons Coulee as seen from the air.

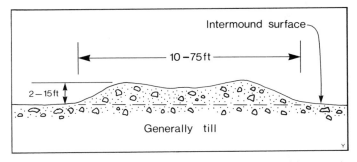

Figure 104. Cross-sectional sketch of representative prairie mound. Dimensions vary within the limits indicated on the figure. Most prairie mounds appear to consist mainly of till, although some are known to have developed in lake-bed sediments.

fields of which extend across much of the prairie landscape. Since no one has ever seen a prairie mound in the process of formation, their origin is in considerable dispute. A well-defined cluster of prairie mounds east of Seven Persons Coulee is shown in *Figure 103*, and a cross-sectional sketch of a typical mound is given in *Figure 104*. Recognition of the existence of prairie mounds in parts of the glaciated Great Plains of North America came relatively late (in the 1940's and 1950's), despite the fact that studies of glacial geology began here a long time ago. It seems probable that not until aerial photographs of the region became generally available was the significance of many of the "hummocks" in areas of so-called hummocky till plain fully appreciated. From the ground, the exact shape of most prairie mounds is obscure, and only extremely careful mapping would reveal the fact that they tend to occur in extensive fields or clusters rather than as isolated individuals. However, an impressive literature on the mounds has accumulated during the past couple of decades, and different investigators have coined a bewildering variety of terms for the feature, including *ice-contact rings, ice-block ridges, humpies, rimmed kettles, doughnuts* (my favorite), *closed disintegration ridges, plains plateaux, moraine plateaux, circular disintegration ridges,* and, of course, *prairie mounds.* As a general rule, geologists tend to be rather conservative in matters political or economic, but when it comes to naming and classifying newly discovered forms and processes their imaginations soar free and unfettered.

The problem with prairie mounds, as might be suspected, is in accounting for their origin. There is general agreement that the mounds could *not* have been formed under masses of

moving ice; their circular or oval shape would seem to preclude this possibility. Those who favor an evolution related to the presence of glacial ice have therefore proposed *two* contrasting theories of origin which can be styled (1) the *ice-press* or *subglacial theory,* and (2) the *ablation, let-down,* or *superglacial theory.* A third hypothesis is based upon the idea that the mounds were formed when glacial ice was not present; this can be termed the *permafrost* or *periglacial theory.*

Briefly, under the *ice-press theory* it is assumed that during a period of deglaciation a mass of stagnant ice, probably not too thick, is resting on a layer of wet, unfrozen till somewhere in the plains. The weight of the overlying ice is believed to be responsible for a pressing or squeezing of saturated sub-glacial material into nearby tunnels, holes, and crevasses in the base of the glacier, and as melting consumes the remnant of dead ice. the irregular landscape of the present is uncovered. Post-glacial modification of the hummocky terrain thus produced is thought to have been only minimal, involving mainly slumping of thin, surficial sheets of till. Critical to this theory of the mounds is the presence in the region of large masses of stagnant or dead ice.

The *ablation theory* also requires the presence of sizable volumes of stagnant ice, but the postulated process of origin is quite different. In this scheme, the material in the prairie mounds is believed to have been contained within the ice or to have been resting on its surface when ablation began. Stagnation of the ice and melting down in place resulted in deposition on the underlying surface of whatever fragmental rock debris may have been present in or on the ice. One feasible model of origin for a single prairie mound is shown in *Figure 105*. Since the mounds tend to occur in clusters or belts rather than as isolated, single features, it seems reasonable to think that numerous mound-producing episodes such as that illustrated in *Figure 105* must have taken place more or less simultaneously in regions in which clusters are found today. With variations, the ablation, or *let-down*, process is believed responsible for the formation of many hummocky till forms, including the curious prairie mounds.

The *periglacial* or *permafrost theory* holds that the mounds formed when the climate was harsh but when glacial ice was not present in the immediate area in which they evolve; presumably this could have been the environmental situation shortly after withdrawal of the last Laurentide glacier. The term "periglacial" literally means "near-glacial", and can refer to (1) a near-glacial climate or (2) a location in close proximity to the edge of glacial ice. Proponents of this theory of origin (and they are not many) suggest that differential freezing of a

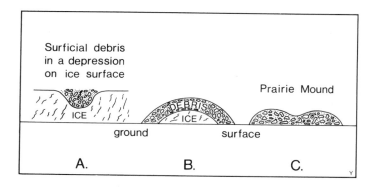

Figure 105. Evolution of a single prairie mound by the let-down or *ablation* process. A. Surficial debris collects in a depression on the surface of a wasting ice mass. B. Melting of the ice lets down the debris onto the underlying ground surface; the debris protects a small mass of ice in the center of the pile from direct solar radiation. C. The protected lens of ice ultimately melts, producing a depression in the pile. The result: Formation of an isolated prairie mound.

mass of saturated till would create unequal pressures below the surface, leading to construction of the mounds by a form of frost-heaving. Permafrost is assumed to have developed for at least a short time following deglaciation, and pockets of unfrozen till, squeezed by encroaching masses of ice, are thought to have been thrust upward to form the mounds. Melting of ice lenses beneath the mounds would subsequently produce the central depressions.

There is no really completely satisfactory way to resolve the problem of which of these theories of origin is the "right" one. Most earth scientists who have investigated the matter tend to reject the permafrost or periglacial hypothesis, but there is no solid concensus regarding which of the other two possibilities is more likely. Probably the most intensive field work on prairie mounds and related features has been done in southern Saskatchewan and adjacent parts of North Dakota, and most geologists who have studied the evidence there have concluded that the superglacial or let-down theory seems best to account for the land forms they have examined in detail.

In any event, the plains of southern Alberta contain thousands of prairie mounds. Much of the southern flank of Milk River Ridge is covered with these forms, and a broad belt of mounds extends eastward from Lethbridge to the north side of the Cypress Hills, best developed between Chin and Etzikom coulees. Small clusters of mounds are also found

between the Milk River valley and the Sweetgrass Hills of Montana. Whatever their origin may have been, prairie mounds make up a significant part of the contemporary surficial topography of the region.

Igneous Intrusions
in the Southern Plains

The conspicuous Sweetgrass Hills of Montana *(Figures 106, 107, and 108)* are familiar to all southern Albertans. They are such a prominent part of the southern skyline because their summits attain remarkable elevations above the surrounding plains. *West Butte*, the highest, reaches 6,983 feet, *East Butte* is but little lower at 6,937 feet, while *Gold Butte* (the pyramidal middle summit) peaks at 6,460 feet. The average elevation of the adjacent prairie is about 3,200 feet, so total relief amounts to more than 3,000 feet. The upper slopes of the buttes are unglaciated; the three summits must have stood above the Laurentide ice as sharp nunataks. Sizable areas of hummocky till are present around all of them, particularly on their northern margins. As is the case in the Cypress Hills, the higher elevation of the Sweetgrass Hills gives rise to lower temperatures and increased precipitation, and a forest of coniferous trees (mainly douglas fir) is present on parts of the buttes.

Figure 106. East Butte of the Sweetgrass Hills. Summit elevation is 6,937 feet.

The Sweetgrass Hills are excellent examples of what geologists call *stocks,* masses of igneous rock emplaced from below that have solidified at depth and have subsequently been uncovered as a result of uplift and erosional removal of the overlying formations. The structural pattern of the Hills is shown in simplified fashion in *Figure 109.* As indicated, the central highland of each butte consists of a mass of igneous rock; the layered sediments intruded by the stocks were tilted up in the process and dip concentrically away from the core in all directions. Radiometric dating of the igneous rock indicates that intrusion occurred in early Tertiary time, some 48 million years ago. In terms of general appearance and structural characteristics, the Sweetgrass Hills are very similar to the larger Bearpaw and Little Rocky mountains of north-central Montana. The Hills are *not* volcanoes, as is sometimes asserted; the igneous rock hardened well below the surface (it is *intrusive* rather than *extrusive*) and has become exposed at the surface by erosional removal of the sedimentary rocks in which emplacement occurred.

Although probably few residents are aware of its presence or significance, southern Alberta has a modest, small-scale replica (or distant relative) of the Sweetgrass Hills. This is *Black Butte (Figure 110),* located south of the Milk River near the former border station of Pinhorn and approximately 15 airline miles northeast of the summit of East Butte. Black Butte is a low, oval-shaped hill rising about 100 feet above the

Figure 107. Gold Butte, Sweetgrass Hills. The top of the central peak reaches 6,460 feet.

Figure 108. West Butte of the Sweetgrass Hills. The top of the high point to the left has an elevation of 6,983 feet.

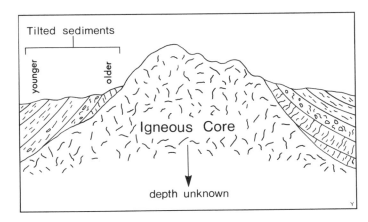

Figure 109. Simplified sketch of structural conditions in the Sweetgrass Hills. Each of the Buttes has a grossly similar structure, although the size of the intrusion is somewhat different in each case.

adjacent plains. It consists of fine-grained, dark-greyish plutonic rock (with distinctive clusters of mica crystals) that contrasts markedly in color with the lighter sandstones of the Oldman formation into which it was intruded. At the eastern end of the butte there is a curious "stack" or "flower pot" of lighter sandstone *(Figure 111)*, a piece of local bedrock apparently hardened by low-grade metamorphism during the episode of intrusion and thus made more resistant to weathering and erosion. Buffalo and cattle have trampled out a depression or moat around its base so that it stands in an isolated position today.

There are a few other minor occurrences of igneous rock in southern Alberta, most in the form of small, nearly vertical dikes, and all topographically inconspicuous. In all probability, the more-or-less continuous cover of glacial debris conceals still more, but it seems unlikely that any of these is of major dimensions.

The Sweetgrass Hills and their extremely limited counterparts in southern Alberta thus represent an element of physiographic diversity in the generally flat plains of the area. Their geologic structure and related geomorphologic prominence provide a welcome addition to the overall regional environment.

Figure 111. Isolated mass of sandstone at the east end of Black Butte.

Figure 110. Black Butte, Alberta's major representative of the cluster of igneous intrusions in the plains.

Summary

It is easy enough to appreciate that the "flat, monotonous plains" of regional fiction and historical journals are, in fact, far from that. The basic geology may be relatively simple, but the details of the landscape include a host of most interesting features.

The geomorphologic history of the southern plains began many tens of millions of years ago with the growth of the ancestral Rockies to the west. For a prolonged period, streams originating in the mountains spread enormous volumes of fragmental debris across the region, material that is today represented by the youngest rocks in the Cypress and Porcupine Hills. But beginning some 25 million years ago, erosion became the primary gradational process in the plains, probably as a result of broad, regional uplift and tilting toward the east. Degradational lowering of the general surface of the plains has continued ever since, although not everywhere at the same rate or with equal success. The Porcupine and

Cypress Hills and Milk River Ridge were not worn down as much as adjacent parts of the region, and thus stand noticeably higher today.

The landscape immediately before Pleistocene glaciation began was evidently a mature one, with broad valleys separated by rolling interstream divides, the overall drainage being toward the east or northeast. Several episodes of Laurentide glaciation ensued, and the character of the landscape was altered significantly, primarily because most of the pre-glacial valleys were filled with till and other non-glacial sediments. Deglaciation exposed the plains to a renewed cycle of valley cutting by the post-glacial rivers, and the prairie surface of the present emerged. Late-glacial and post-glacial gradational activity by running water, the wind, and gravity thus accounts for the larger and smaller land forms, all of which have been cut into or superimposed upon the surface uncovered as glaciation waned and finally ended.

To the observer who really sees (and understands what is being seen), the "monotonous plains" are non-existent, a figment of somebody else's imagination. Study of the modern regional landscape reveals a long and diversified history of development, the latest chapter of which is still being composed. An understanding of that history, based upon knowledge of how the forms of the present came to be as they are, must lead to a rejection of the idea that this landscape is dull and uninspiring.

* * * * *

CHAPTER 6
IN RETROSPECT

Pointing the reader in the direction of achieving a *general* understanding of the landscapes of southern Alberta has been the primary goal of this book. A secondary aim has been to make as many people as possible aware of the great diversity of geologic and geomorphologic features in our part of the province, an appreciation of which does not require a university degree in the geological sciences. The value one attaches to knowledge of the surrounding physical environment is, of course, a purely personal, subjective matter, but I persist in believing that literally anyone can benefit from such knowledge, directly in a few cases, indirectly in virtually all. Life would be a pretty dull affair, in my judgment, without some interest in and understanding of the natural world in which we find ourselves. Residents of southern Alberta are fortunate indeed to be living in such an interesting part of North America.

Figure 113. Foothills scene near Longview.

By "understanding" a landscape I mean being able to recognize its larger geological structural characteristics and the land forms made by the various gradational processes acting through time (including the present). I do *not* mean being able to identify to the last trace element and rare mineral every obscure rock type one may encounter in the field; few professional geologists possess that particular ability. Nor do I mean having at the tip of one's tongue all the latest technical jargon with which geology and geomorphology are becoming increasingly cursed. The danger is very real, or so it seems to me, that many a potential student, formal or informal, will be completely turned off by the necessity of having to learn a new language simply to be able to comprehend what the earth scientist is talking about. The world is already burdened by too many semantic problems, and at times one gets the impression that geologists are working overtime to add to the difficulties. Most land forms and geologic processes can be adequately described in plain, straightforward language, and an attempt has been made to do just that in this book.

Figure 112. The Alberta Rockies south of the Crowsnest Pass corridor.

Figure 114. Rolling till plain in southeastern Alberta. The boulder is a glacial erratic — a piece of granite from the Canadian Shield.

unique character *(Figure 115)*, and their topographic prominence adds a degree of vertical diversity to a primarily horizontal world.

Inevitably, my discussions of the landscapes of southern Alberta will have slighted or overlooked many favorite topographic and scenic features of this part of the province. Little has been said, for example, about evolution of most of the modern river valleys; the Chain Lakes were completely ignored, as was Red Rock Canyon in Waterton Lakes National Park. And there are undoubtedly many other "special" places not mentioned herein. The reason is comparatively simple — the decision to include or to omit specific landscape elements was, of necessity, based on limitations of time, limitations of space, and my own very real personal ignorance of large parts of the area. The book is obviously selective rather than totally comprehensive. But the fundamental purpose has been to generate an interest in and enthusiasm for looking at landscapes as something other than simply "pretty" or "boring" scenery. Our scenery is worth considerably more than passing attention, and if even the beginnings of an appreciation of landscape history have been stimulated by this volume, it can be counted a success.

The three basic geomorphologic regions of southern Alberta — the mountains, foothills, and plains — owe their distinctiveness to differing combinations of the internal and external processes responsible for shaping of the earth's surface. Tectonic activity has been most pronounced in the Rockies, and the result is a landscape dominated by steep slopes, very great relief, and some of the most spectacular scenery in our part of the world *(Figure 112)*. Foothills landscapes, in contrast, reflect a much lesser intensity of operation of the gradational and tectonic forces *(Figure 113)*; here, slopes are gentler, relief is measurable in hundreds rather than thousands of feet, and the overall visual impression is of a subdued topography, less vigorously affected by the agents of geological change.

The largest of the physiographic units of southern Alberta, the plains, appears to some to be flat, monotonous, and generally devoid of interest, but such an impression would be wrong, utterly wrong. What makes a landscape more than simply space through which to pass is a perception of its natural history, and the plains have certainly had their share of variety of geomorphologic processes and change. The seeming flatness of much of the plains *(Figure 114)* is illusory; in most of the region there *is* surface relief, although quite apparently it is much less developed than that of the foothills and mountains. The higher parts of the plains province each have a

Figure 115. Northern slope of Milk River Ridge at harvest time.

SUGGESTED REFERENCES

The following books and other references are a selected sample from a much larger literature. Most are still in print and are obtainable from the appropriate publishers. Many of those that are no longer generally available can be found in university, college, research station, and city libraries within the province.

General Geology and Geomorphology

American Geological Institute. *Glossary of Geology.* Washington, D.C., American Geological Institute, 1972.

Bloom, Arthur L. *The Surface of the Earth.* Englewood Cliffs, New Jersey, Prentice-Hall, Inc., 1969.

Easterbrook, Don J. *Principles of Geomorphology.* New York, McGraw-Hill Book Company, 1969.

Flint, Richard F. and Skinner, Brian J. *Physical Geology.* New York, John Wiley and Sons, Inc. 1974.

Gilluly, James, Waters, Aaron C., and Woodford, A.O. *Principles of Geology.* San Francisco, W.H. Freeman and Company, 4th edition, 1975.

Hamblin, W.K. *The Earth's Dynamic Systems: A Textbook in Physical Geology.* Minneapolis, Burgess Publishing Company, 1975.

Leet, L. Don and Judson, Sheldon. *Physical Geology.* Englewood Cliffs, New Jersey, Prentice-Hall, Inc., 4th edition, 1971.

Longwell, Chester R., Flint, Richard F., and Sanders, John E. *Physical Geology.* New York, John Wiley and Sons, Inc., 1969.

Press, Frank and Siever, Raymond. *Earth.* San Francisco, W.H. Freeman and Company, 1974.

Ruhe, Robert V. *Geomorphology: Geomorphic Processes and Surficial Geology.* Boston, Houghton Mifflin Company, 1975.

Shelton, John S. *Geology Illustrated.* San Francisco, W.H. Freeman and Company, 1966.

Thornbury, William D. *Principles of Geomorphology.* New York, John Wiley and Sons, Inc., 2nd edition, 1969.

Tuttle, Sherwood D. *Landforms and Landscapes.* Dubuque, Iowa, Wm. C. Brown Company Publishers, 1970.

Agents of Gradation

Bagnold, R.A. *The Physics of Blown Sand and Desert Dunes.* London, Methuen and Company, 1941 (reprinted 1960).

Bascom, Willard. *Waves and Beaches: The Dynamics of the Ocean Surface.* Garden City, New York, Anchor Books, Doubleday and Company, Inc., 1964.

Morisawa, Marie. *Streams: Their Dynamics and Morphology.* New York, McGraw-Hill Book Company, 1968.

Price, R.J. *Glacial and Fluvioglacial Landforms.* Edinburgh, Oliver and Boyd, 1973.

Sharpe, C.F. Stewart. *Landslides and Related Phenomena: A Study of Mass-Movements of Soil and Rock.* New York, Cooper Square Publishers, Inc., 1968 (reprint of 1938 edition).

The New Geology: Continental Drift, Sea-Floor Spreading, and Plate Tectonics

Hallam, A. *A Revolution in the Earth Sciences: From Continental Drift to Plate Tectonics.* Oxford, Clarendon Press, 1973.

Scientific American (various authors). *Continents Adrift.* San Francisco, W.H. Freeman and Company, 1972 (readings from *Scientific American*).

Sullivan, Walter. *Continents in Motion: The New Earth Debate.* New York, McGraw-Hill Book Company, 1974.

Takeuchi, H., Uyeda, S., and Kanamori, H. *Debate About the Earth: Approach to Geophysics through Analysis of Continental Drift.* San Francisco, Freeman, Cooper and Co., revised edition, 1970.

Tarling, D.H. and Tarling, M. P. *Continental Drift: A Study of the Earth's Moving Surface.* Middlesex, England, Penguin Books, Ltd., 1972 (reprint of 1971 edition).

Wegener, Alfred. *The Origin of Continents and Oceans.* New York, Dover Publications, Inc., 1966 (translation and reprint of 4th German edition, 1929).

Alberta and Canada

Alberta, University of, Department of Geography. *Atlas of Alberta.* Edmonton, University of Alberta Press in association with University of Toronto Press, 1969.

Alt, D.D. and Hyndman, D.W. *Rocks, Ice & Water: The Geology of Waterton-Glacier Park.* Missoula, Montana, Mountain Press Publishing Company, 1973.

Atwood, Wallace W. *The Physiographic Provinces of North America.* Boston, Ginn and Company, 1940.

Baird, D.M. *Waterton Lakes National Park: Lakes Amid the Mountains.* Ottawa, Geological Survey of Canada, Misc. Report 10, 1964.

Bally, W.W., Gordy, P.L., and Stewart, G.A. "Structure, Seismic Data, and Orogenic Evolution of Southern Canadian Rocky Mountains." *Bulletin of Canadian Petroleum Geology,* Vol. 14, No. 3, pp. 337-381, 1966.

Beaty, C.B. "Geographical Distribution of Post-Glacial Slumping in Southern Alberta." *Canadian Geotechnical Journal,* Vol. 9, No. 2, pp. 219-224, 1972.

Beaty, C.B. "Coulee Alignment and the Wind in Southern Alberta, Canada." *Bulletin,* Geological Society of America, Vol. 86, No. 1, pp. 119-128, 1975.

Bird, J. Brian. *The Natural Landscapes of Canada: A Study in Regional Earth Science.* Toronto, Wiley Publishers of Canada, Ltd., 1972.

Blackadar, R.G. and Vincent, L.E. *Focus on Canadian Landscapes (Regards sur les Paysages Canadiens).* Ottawa, Geological Survey of Canada, Miscellaneous Report 19, 1973.

Bostok, H.A. *Physiographic Subdivisions of Canada.* In: *Geology and Economic Minerals of Canada* (5th edition). Ottawa, Geological Survey of Canada, 1970.

Clark, Thomas H. and Stearn, Colin W. *Geological Evolution of North America.* New York, The Ronald Press Company, 2nd edition, 1968.

Farvolden, R.N. *Bedrock Channels of Southern Alberta.* In: *Early Contributions to the Groundwater Hydrology of Alberta.* Edmonton, Research Council of Alberta, Bulletin 12, 1963.

Geological Survey of Canada. *Short Papers on Quaternary Research in Canada.* Ottawa, Geological Survey of Canada, 1969.

Gravenor, C.P. and Bayrock, L.A. *Glacial Deposits of Alberta.* In: *Soils in Canada* (revised edition). Toronto, Royal Society of Canada, Special Publication 9, 1965.

Green, R. (compiler). *Geological Map of Alberta.* Edmonton, Research Council of Alberta, Map 35, 1972.

Hardy, W.G. (editor). *Alberta: A Natural History.* Edmonton, M.G. Hurtig Company, Ltd., 1967.

Hunt, Charles B. *Natural Regions of the United States and Canada.* San Francisco, W.H. Freeman and Company, 1974.

Irish, E.J.W. *Geology — Foremost.* Ottawa, Geological Survey of Canada, Map 22—1967, 1968.

Irish, E.J.W. *Geology — Gleichen.* Ottawa, Geological Survey of Canada, Map 19—1967, 1968.

Irish, E.J.W. *Geology — Lethbridge.* Ottawa, Geological Survey of Canada, Map 20—1967, 1968.

Irish, E.J.W. *Geology — Medicine Hat.* Ottawa, Geological Survey of Canada, Map 21—1967, 1968.

Jankunis, Frank J. (editor). *Southern Alberta: A Regional Perspective.* Lethbridge, The University of Lethbridge, 1972.

King, Phillip B. *The Evolution of North America.* Princeton, New Jersey, Princeton University Press, 1959.

McCrossan, R.G. and Glaister, R.P. (editors). *Geological History of Western Canada.* Calgary, Alberta Society of Petroleum Geologists, 1964 (reprinted 1970).

McPherson, R.A. (compiler). *Surficial Geology — Medicine Hat* (map). Edmonton, Research Council of Alberta, 1972.

Nelson, J.G. and Chambers, M.J. *Process and Method in Canadian Geography: Geomorphology* (selected papers). Toronto, Methuen Publishers, 1969.

Nelson, S.J. *The Face of Time: The Geological History of Western Canada.* Calgary, Alberta Society of Petroleum Geologists, 1970.

Prest, V.K. *Retreat of Wisconsin and Recent Ice in North America.* Ottawa, Geological Survey of Canada, Map 1257A, 1969.

Russell, L.S. and Landes, R.W. *Geology of the Southern Alberta Plains.* Ottawa, Geological Survey of Canada, Memoir 221, 1940.

Smith, P.J. (editor). *Studies in Canadian Geography: The Prairie Provinces.* Toronto, University of Toronto Press, 1972.

Stalker, A. MacS. *The Erratics Train: Foothills of Alberta.* Ottawa, Geological Survey of Canada, Bulletin 37, 1956.

Stalker, A. MacS. *Surficial Geology – High River.* Ottawa, Geological Survey of Canada, Map 14–1957, 1957.

Stalker, A. MacS. *Surficial Geology – Fort Macleod.* Ottawa, Geological Survey of Canada, Map 21–1958, 1959.

Stalker, A. MacS. *Buried Valleys in Central and Southern Alberta.* Ottawa, Geological Survey of Canada, Paper 60-32, 1961.

Stalker, A. MacS. *Surficial Geology – Fernie* (east half). Ottawa, Geological Survey of Canada, Map 31–1961, 1962.

Stalker, A. MacS. *Surficial Geology – Lethbridge.* Ottawa, Geological Survey of Canada, Map 41–1962, 1962.

Stalker, A. MacS. *Quaternary Stratigraphy in Southern Alberta.* Ottawa, Geological Survey of Canada, Paper 62-34, 1963.

Stalker, A. MacS. *Surficial Geology of Blood Indian Reserve, No. 148, Alberta.* Ottawa, Geological Survey of Canada, Paper 63-25, 1963.

Stalker, A. MacS. *Surficial Geology – Bassano.* Ottawa, Geological Survey of Canada, Map 5–1965, 1965.

Stalker, A. MacS. *Quaternary Stratigraphy in Southern Alberta Report II: Sections Near Medicine Hat.* Ottawa, Geological Survey of Canada, Paper 69-26, 1969.

Westgate, J.A. *Surficial Geology of the Foremost-Cypress Hills Area, Alberta.* Edmonton, Research Council of Alberta, Bulletin 22, 1968.

Williams, M.Y. and Dyer, W.S. *Geology of Southern Alberta and Southwestern Saskatchewan.* Ottawa, Geological Survey of Canada, Memoir 163, 1930.

Topographic maps of southern Alberta are available from:

Canada Map Office
615 Booth Street
Ottawa, Canada K1A 0E9

Write to this agency for indexes of available maps, instructions on how to order, and current prices.

Aerial photographs of the region are available from:

National Air Photo Library
Department of Energy, Mines and Resources
Ottawa, Canada K1A 0E9

Write to this agency for indexes of available photography, instructions on how to order, and current prices.

Born in Chicago, Illinois, Dr. Chester B. Beaty, professor of geography, has been with The University of Lethbridge since 1969. He received his B.A. from Louisiana State University in 1948, his M.A. from LSU in 1950, and his Ph.D. from the University of California, Berkeley, in 1960. His primary research interest is geomorphology — the study of land forms — but he has a strong secondary interest in resource allocation decisions.

Born in Montreal, Quebec, Mr. G. Stanley Young has been with the department of geography at The University of Lethbridge since 1970. He received his B.Sc. from the University of Calgary in 1970 and his M.A. from the University of Oregon in 1977. His primary interest is cartography.